Home Guide to
Solar Heating and Cooling

Home Guide to
Solar Heating and Cooling

by Jackson Hand

Drawings by
Danmark & Michaels

POPULAR SCIENCE

HARPER & ROW

New York, Evanston, San Francisco, London

Contents

Appendices

Preface

I'VE TALKED ABOUT solar energy for home heating and cooling with many people recently—most of them pretty handy around the house. Much to my surprise, their attitude has been that solar energy is for the experts—way over the head and beyond the skills of the typical homeowner. Solar energy someday, probably, they seem to feel—but not yet for the average person.

It is because these reactions are so far wrong that I have put together this book on solar energy as it can be used in just about any residential situation—in just about any environment.

The book bypasses the "science" of solar energy and puts forth the simple facts. The objective is to point out the basics of a natural phenomenon that belongs to all of us and is within the reach of all of us: heat from the sun.

With these basics covered, the book further exposes the simplicity of solar energy adaptation by going into how-to details for making a system using ordinary homeowner how-to tools and know-how. In fact, through do-it-yourself adoption, solar energy will make its fastest growth. Already, producers of systems are making materials and components available to the homeowner, and the number of solar energy sources is growing, neighborhood by neighborhood.

This book tells you how you can make your own system, using everyday materials and methods, at surprisingly low costs, with results that will save a great amount of money that would have to be spent for one of the most increasingly expensive items in household operation—heating and cooling fuels.

JACKSON HAND
Westport, Connecticut

Introducing Solar Energy

THERE WAS A TIME when mankind's only source of heat was the sun. Then man learned how to build a fire and use it for heating. Wood provided the fuel. Time moved on, and man discovered that fossil fuels (coal, oil, and natural gas) would produce heat too. He also discovered electricity and learned that it produced heat when it traveled through the right kinds of wire. Mankind then became well supplied and content with the heating energy provided by fossil fuels—and the electricity generated in their use.

But there came a day when these sources presented problems. They were getting expensive. They were hard to transport from the source to the place of use. *And they were becoming scarce.* In fact, there were omens of the complete depletion of fossil fuels. Mankind then began to look to the sun as a source of heat and energy. Within a few years, this interest in the sun became a worldwide revolution.

Today, there are thousands of homes for which the sun provides the heat needed for room comfort, or for hot water requirements, or for both. In many of those homes, heat from the sun also provides the energy used for air conditioning.

The owners of those homes are taking advantage of an energy source that is free—and that promises to continue in enormous supply for another three or four billion years. The sun is so powerful a source of heat that its energy hitting the earth over a single 24-hour period could, in theory, meet man's energy needs for a whole year. All that is needed is efficient and affordable methods of collecting that heat and putting it to work. And in the current era of energy shortages, research is producing increasingly effective means of putting the sun to work in the home.

THE PURPOSE OF THIS BOOK. Because the science of home solar heating is relatively new, many homeowners have not paid much attention to the way solar heat can serve them. This book will explain the principles of solar energy utilization: how solar energy can be used in your home; how it is installed; and, most important, how you can design and construct your own system.

In the following pages, you will find complete coverage of the kinds of systems available and which will best suit your own needs. You will find useful discussion of the various ways you can use the energy efficiently and economically. And you will find information regarding the type of residence—architecturally speaking—that will best accept solar heat. This will include what modifications, if any, may be necessary in your present home.

THE ABCs OF SOLAR ENERGY. Solar energy is collected—that is, the sun's rays are "tapped"—by heat absorption. This is a simple matter, as you will realize if you have ever placed your hand on the hood of a black automobile sitting in the sun. The black surface absorbs the heat.

In solar heat collectors, this absorption is brought up to a high efficiency

As proof that solar collectors are not such a new phenomenon, this photograph of a solar-collector factory was taken in the 1920s. The plant, destroyed by fire in 1942, was that of the Solar Water Heater Company of Miami, Florida.

Solar heating components are mass produced today. These collector plates are coming off the assembly lines at the PPG plant in Pittsburgh.

by special designs. Basically, however, the heat is collected in sheets of metal painted black.

The heat thus collected is made useful by means of a liquid that is heated by the hot black metal or else by air that is heated. The liquid is most frequently just water, although certain situations demand chemicals or chemically treated water. When air is the transmission medium, the system is usually little different from warm-air heating systems used for furnaces. The principal difference is the source of heat, which is a solar-heat collector instead of a coal, oil, or wood burner.

In heated water systems, the water is delivered to elements that utilize the heat or to tanks where the heat is stored. In a majority of cases, the system produces only hot water for the kitchen sink or the bath. In other applications, the water is used to heat the entire house—or a part of the house, or an adjacent building, or even a swimming pool. Solar heat can also be used to operate air conditioners, cooling the house in the summer as effectively as it heats it in the winter.

3

There are, also, completely passive heat collecting systems which involve little or no mechanization. The heat is brought into the house through modified windows. Then the walls, floors, and other structures within the house store the heat for later use.

WHEN YOU DO IT YOURSELF. The basics of solar heat collecting are so simple that any home handyman can put together a system of his own. As well, some of the components can be homemade. But for some of the more sophisticated systems, components are a little beyond a handyman's reach. When this is the case, the components are available from a wide range of sources, listed in the back of this book.

Before you make any move toward solar energy utilization, examine this book carefully. It will help you select the most useful, efficient, and economical systems, components, and methods. Using this book, you'll become enough of an expert to determine which is the best system for you and your environment.

HOME MORTGAGE AND SOLAR ENERGY. The National Solar Heating & Cooling Information Center has been established by the U.S. Department of Housing & Urban Development, in cooperation with the Energy Research & Development Administration. The Center can provide information about the location of solar homes in your area; supply the names of architects, builders, and manufacturers who specialize in solar; and provide publications that may be of help to you in making decisions about solar heating for your present home or the home you plan to build.

One of the most significant of these publications is "Home Mortgage Lending and Solar Energy." For a copy of this booklet and other information, write Solar Heating, P. O. Box 1607, Rockville, MD 20850.

1 | Is Solar Heating for You?

No MATTER WHERE YOU LIVE or what your living situation may be, solar heating can serve you. Your chief options include how much solar heat you want to use and what you use it for.

Solar heating is easiest in the South, where it is least needed. It is most difficult in the North, where the need is greatest. However, the system you would use in the South would cost much less to install than that required in the North. In the Deep South you might think of solar energy mainly as a means of heating water for your kitchen and bath, and secondarily as a source of home heating. In the Far North, it can heat your domestic water and go a long way toward heating the house—although it would require some support from an auxiliary heating system that burns fuel.

To determine your needs, you won't have to do any guesswork. The Department of Energy has established "weather-map" solar-heating factors for the home owner. The factors are based on weather data over the years, and although they might run a little amiss in unusually mild or cold winters, they do give a reliable picture of the typical heating needs, state-by-state, city-by-city. The DOE factors give you standards for decision-making in two categories: Degree Days and Amount of Energy.

Degree days. This factor indicates the total number of degrees in a given month—or an entire year—the average daily temperature is below 65°F. For example, if the average temperature for a given day is 50°F, its degree-day rating is 15. When there are several days during the month with sub-65° temperatures, their degree-day ratings are added together to arrive at degree days for the month. The total of monthly degree-days becomes the annual rating. See the table of degree days at the end of this chapter.

To pick some extremes for comparison from the accompanying table, Miami Beach, Florida, has an annual degree-day rating of 141. New York has 4871. Spokane, Washington, is rated at 6655. San Diego, California—1439. Moving up the Mississippi, New Orleans is rated 1385 annually; St. Louis is 4900; Minneapolis is 8382. These figures indicate that utilization of

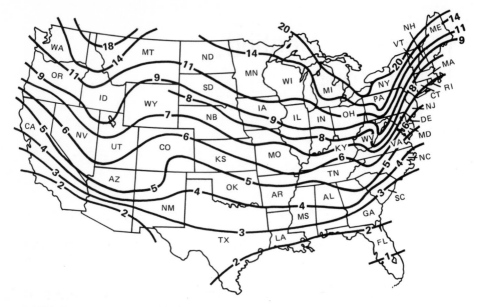

This map shows the relative difficulty of solar heating in 12 belts throughout the U.S. The higher the number, the larger the solar collector's capacity must be.

solar energy will *cost the least* in warmer parts of the country, while it will *save the most* in colder parts of the country. Either way, the conservation of standard fuels makes solar energy worthwhile for everybody.

Amount of energy. The second factor measured by the DOE is the amount of solar radiation that strikes the earth. The accompanying map shows the pattern across the country. As the map shows, the greatest amount of solar energy falls in the Southwest, the smallest amount in the Northeast. However, during the winter months, some northern areas receive relatively greater amounts of solar energy, due to clearer skies.

Manufacturers of solar heating equipment can provide you with figures relating to the cost of installing an efficient system in any region, or in any city. Their figures are based on the degree-days and the solar radiation ratings.

ADD-ON SOLAR HEATING. There are other factors you should consider —in addition to the weather-and-sunshine. If you are living in your own home and are thinking about installing solar heating equipment (the industry term is "retrofitting"), the exact nature of the house is important. Such factors as architecture, construction, orientation, and environment must be taken into consideration. Let's look at them one at a time.

Architecture. Most residential designs can be retrofitted for solar collectors. The ideal collector is mounted at a slant that is well suited to most roof pitches. An angle equal to your location's latitude plus or minus 10 degrees will produce acceptable performance from most collectors. If the pitch is too steep or too flat, modifications in the mounting are simple. Even if the roof is flat, the collector can be mounted at the required angle, or special collectors can be used that lie flat but have several "fins" at the proper angle. About the only unusable roof would be a single-pitch roof that faces north.

Some homes may not have a pitched roof that is large enough to hold the required area of collecting elements. As a rough rule of thumb, you can figure that a collector large enough to heat your home will have an area approximately half that of the heated floor area. A house with 1200 square feet of floor area would need a 600-foot-square solar collector—or a little less. When the roof doesn't offer that much square footage, it is common practice to extend the collector beyond the ridge. (Note: For an accurate determination of the collector area needed, it's also necessary to consider heat-loss characteristics of your own house. This is covered in Chapter 3.)

Many people with unsuitable roof areas meet collector area requirements by installing a collector that leans against a side or end of the house. Or collectors can be mounted on an adjoining building or simply installed in the yard. In addition, there are specially engineered systems which have heat collectors mounted vertically. These become part of the wall construction of the house. Details of this construction are given in following chapters.

If you are thinking of a new home, you should include solar heating in the overall package. Today's architects and house planners understand the requirements, so more and more houses go up with solar heating taken for granted. In many cases, the demand for solar energy may influence the entire design of the house. In others, classic house designs may be modified as need be to make solar heating possible. Either way, solar heating will add to the value of the house and will earn back its cost in a few years. Authorities say that any house without solar heating facilities will be obsolete before long.

Construction. It goes without saying that the house to be retrofitted with solar energy equipment must be adequately insulated, but good insulation should be a priority regardless of the heating system used. In any existing home, full advantage should be taken of today's excellent insulating materials and methods. This must include careful attention to air leaks around doors and windows and other areas of heat loss.

Orientation. There isn't much you can do about the direction an existing house faces. Ideally, there should be a roof or wall facing south. When you

(*Text continues on page 14.*)

The map on pages 8 and 9 shows the amount of solar heat that hits the United States in different regions. It is expressed in daily "Langleys." A Langley equals about 3.7 Btu per square foot. Heat at specific locations is noted on the table beginning on page 10.

MEAN DAILY SOLAR RADIATION (Langleys)

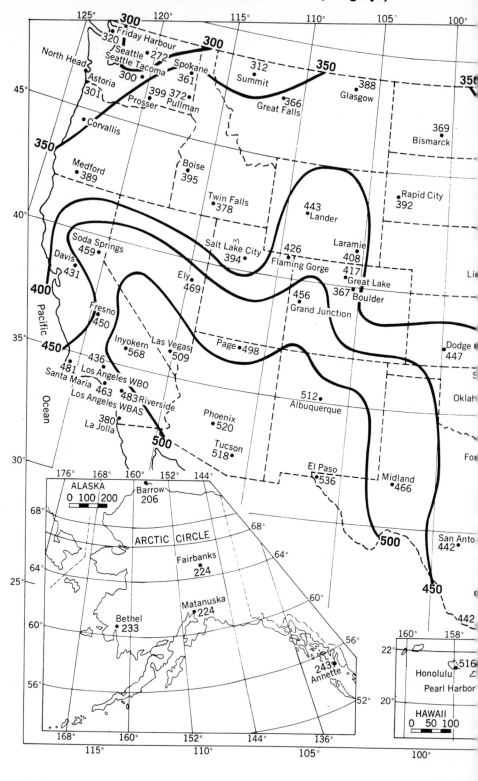

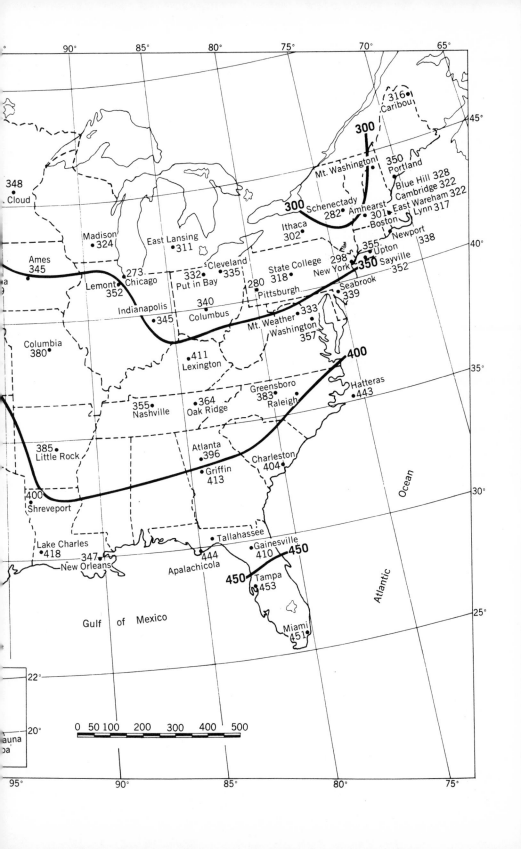

MEAN DAILY SOLAR RADIATION (Langleys)

STATE AND STATION	JAN.	FEB.	MAR.	APR.	MAY	JUNE	JULY	AUG.	SEPT.	OCT.	NOV.	DEC.	ANNUAL
ALASKA													
Annette	63	115	236	364	437	438	438	341	258	122	59	41	243
Bethel	38	108	282	444	457	454	376	252	202	115	44	22	233
Fairbanks	16	71	213	376	461	504	434	317	180	82	26	6	224
ARIZONA													
Page	300	382	526	618	695	707	680	596	516	402	310	243	498
Phoenix	301	409	526	638	724	739	658	613	566	449	344	281	520
Tucson	315	391	540	655	729	699	626	588	570	442	356	305	518
ARKANSAS													
Little Rock	188	260	353	446	523	559	556	518	439	343	244	187	385
CALIFORNIA													
Davis	174	257	390	528	625	694	682	612	493	347	222	148	431
Fresno	184	289	427	552	647	702	682	621	510	376	250	161	450
Inyokern (China Lake)	306	412	562	683	772	819	772	729	635	467	363	300	568
LaJolla	244	302	397	457	506	487	497	464	389	320	277	221	380
Los Angeles WBAS	248	331	470	515	572	596	641	581	503	373	289	241	463
Riverside	275	367	478	541	623	680	673	618	535	407	319	270	483
COLORADO													
Boulder	201	268	401	460	460	525	520	439	412	310	222	182	367
Grand Junction	227	324	434	546	615	708	676	595	514	373	260	212	456
Grand Lake (Granby)	212	313	423	512	552	632	600	505	476	361	234	184	417
DIST. OF COLUMBIA													
Washington (C.O.)	174	266	344	411	551	494	536	446	375	299	211	166	356
American University	158	231	322	398	467	510	496	440	364	278	192	141	333
Silver Hill	177	247	342	438	513	555	511	457	391	293	202	156	357
FLORIDA													
Apalachicola	298	367	441	535	603	578	529	511	456	413	332	262	444
Gainesville	267	343	427	517	579	521	488	483	418	347	300	233	410
Miami Airport	349	415	489	540	553	532	532	505	440	384	353	316	451
Tampa	327	391	474	539	596	574	534	494	452	400	356	300	453
GEORGIA													
Atlanta	218	290	380	488	533	562	532	508	416	344	268	211	396
Griffin	234	295	385	522	570	577	556	522	435	368	283	201	413

STATE AND STATION	JAN.	FEB.	MAR.	APR.	MAY	JUNE	JULY	AUG.	SEPT.	OCT.	NOV.	DEC.	ANNUAL
HAWAII													
Honolulu	363	422	516	559	617	615	615	612	573	507	426	371	516
Mauna Loa Obs.	522	576	680	689	727	*	703	642	602	560	504	481	—
Pearl Harbor	359	400	487	529	573	566	598	567	539	466	386	343	484
IDAHO													
Boise	138	236	342	485	585	636	670	576	460	301	182	124	395
Twin Falls	163	240	355	462	552	592	602	540	432	286	176	131	378
ILLINOIS													
Chicago	96	147	227	331	424	458	473	403	313	207	120	76	273
Lemont	170	242	340	402	506	553	540	498	398	275	165	138	352
INDIANA													
Indianapolis	144	213	316	396	488	543	541	490	405	293	177	132	345
IOWA													
Ames	174	253	326	403	480	541	436	460	367	274	187	143	345
KANSAS													
Dodge City	255	316	418	528	568	650	642	592	493	380	285	234	447
Manhattan	192	264	345	433	527	551	531	526	410	292	227	156	371
KENTUCKY													
Lexington	172	263	357	480	581	628	617	563	494	357	245	174	411
LOUISIANA													
Lake Charles	245	306	397	481	555	591	526	511	449	402	300	250	418
New Orleans	214	259	335	412	449	443	417	416	383	357	278	198	347
Shreveport	232	292	384	446	558	557	578	528	414	354	254	205	400
MAINE													
Caribou	133	231	364	400	476	470	508	448	336	212	111	107	316
Portland	152	235	352	409	514	539	561	488	383	278	157	137	350
MASSACHUSETTS													
Amherst	116	*	300	*	431	514	*	—	—	—	152	124	—
Blue Hill	153	228	319	389	469	510	502	449	354	266	162	135	328
Boston	129	194	290	350	445	483	486	411	334	235	136	115	301
East Wareham	140	218	305	385	452	508	495	436	365	258	163	140	322

(*continued*)

(MEAN DAILY SOLAR RADIATION TABLE Continued)

STATE AND STATION	JAN.	FEB.	MAR.	APR.	MAY	JUNE	JULY	AUG.	SEPT.	OCT.	NOV.	DEC.	ANNUAL
MICHIGAN													
East Lansing	121	210	309	359	483	547	540	466	373	255	136	108	311
Sault Ste. Marie	130	225	356	416	523	557	573	472	322	216	105	96	333
MINNESOTA													
St. Cloud	168	260	368	426	496	535	557	486	366	237	146	124	348
MISSOURI													
Columbia (C. O.)	173	251	340	434	530	574	574	522	453	322	225	158	380
Univ. of Missouri	166	248	324	429	501	560	583	509	417	324	177	146	365
MONTANA													
Glasgow	154	258	385	466	568	605	645	561	410	267	184	116	388
Great Falls	140	232	366	434	528	583	639	532	407	264	154	112	366
Summit	122	162	268	414	462	493	560	510	354	216	102	76	312
NEBRASKA													
Lincoln	188	259	350	416	494	544	568	484	396	296	199	159	363
North Omaha	193	299	365	463	516	546	568	519	410	298	204	170	379
NEVADA													
Ely	236	339	468	563	625	712	647	618	518	394	289	218	469
Las Vegas	277	384	519	621	702	748	675	627	551	429	318	258	509
NEW JERSEY													
Seabrook	157	227	318	403	482	527	509	455	385	278	192	140	339
NEW HAMPSHIRE													
Mt. Washington	117	218	238	°	°	°	—	—	°	°	°	96	—
NEW MEXICO													
Albuquerque	303	386	511	618	686	726	683	626	554	438	334	276	512
NEW YORK													
Ithaca	116	194	272	334	440	501	515	453	346	231	120	96	302
N. Y. Central Park	130	199	290	369	432	470	459	389	331	242	147	115	298
Schnectady	130	200	273	338	413	448	441	397	299	218	128	104	282
NORTH CAROLINA													
Greensboro	200	276	354	469	531	564	544	485	406	322	243	197	383
Hatteras	238	317	426	569	635	652	625	562	471	358	282	214	443
Raleigh	235	302	°	466	494	564	535	476	379	307	235	199	—

STATE AND STATION	JAN.	FEB.	MAR.	APR.	MAY	JUNE	JULY	AUG.	SEPT.	OCT.	NOV.	DEC.	ANNUAL
NORTH DAKOTA													
Bismarck	157	250	356	447	550	590	617	516	390	272	161	124	369
OHIO													
Cleveland	125	183	303	286	502	562	562	494	278	289	141	115	335
Columbus	128	200	297	391	471	562	542	477	422	286	176	129	340
Put-in-Bay	126	204	302	386	468	544	561	487	382	275	144	109	332
OKLAHOMA													
Oklahoma City	251	319	409	494	536	615	610	593	487	377	291	240	436
Stillwater	205	289	390	454	504	600	596	545	455	354	269	209	405
OREGON													
Astoria	90	162	270	375	492	469	539	461	354	209	111	79	301
Corvallis	89	*	287	406	517	570	676	558	397	235	144	80	—
Medford	116	215	336	482	592	652	698	605	447	279	149	93	389
PENNSYLVANIA													
Pittsburgh	94	169	216	317	429	491	497	409	339	207	118	77	280
State College	133	201	295	380	456	518	511	444	358	256	149	118	318
RHODE ISLAND													
Newport	155	232	334	405	477	527	513	455	377	271	176	139	338
SOUTH CAROLINA													
Charleston	252	314	388	512	551	564	520	501	404	338	286	225	404
SOUTH DAKOTA													
Rapid City	183	277	400	482	532	585	590	541	435	315	204	158	392
TENNESSEE													
Nashville	149	228	322	432	503	551	530	473	403	308	208	150	355
Oak Ridge	161	239	331	450	518	551	526	478	416	318	213	163	364
TEXAS													
Brownsville	297	341	402	456	564	610	627	568	475	411	296	263	442
El Paso	333	430	547	654	714	729	666	640	576	460	372	313	536
Ft. Worth	250	320	427	488	562	651	613	593	503	403	306	245	445
San Antonio	279	347	417	445	541	612	639	585	493	398	295	256	442
UTAH													
Flaming Gorge	238	298	443	522	565	650	599	538	425	352	262	215	426
Salt Lake City	163	256	354	479	570	621	620	551	446	316	204	146	394

(*continued*)

(MEAN DAILY SOLAR RADIATION TABLE Continued)

STATE AND STATION	JAN.	FEB.	MAR.	APR.	MAY	JUNE	JULY	AUG.	SEPT.	OCT.	NOV.	DEC.	ANNUAL
VIRGINIA													
Mt. Weather	172	274	338	414	508	525	510	430	375	281	202	168	350
WASHINGTON													
North Head	*	167	257	432	509	487	486	436	321	205	122	77	—
Univ. of Washington	67	126	245	364	445	461	496	435	299	170	93	59	272
Seattle-Tacoma	75	139	265	403	503	511	566	452	324	188	104	64	300
Spokane	119	204	321	474	563	596	665	556	404	225	131	75	361
WISCONSIN													
Madison	148	220	313	394	466	514	531	452	348	241	145	115	324
WYOMING													
Lander	226	324	452	548	587	678	651	586	472	354	239	196	443
Laramie	216	295	424	508	554	643	606	536	438	324	229	186	408

NOTES: * Denotes only one year of data for the month—no means computed. — No data for the month (or incomplete data for the year).

(Text continued from page 7.)

build from scratch, this can be basic to your plans. The ideal direction is not always due south; it can be a little east or west of south. If early-morning haze or fog is prevalent, such as in coastal regions, an angle west of south may actually provide a better performing solar heating system. So the ideal angle depends on your locale. In some cases, this angle may not conform to zoning requirements that house fronts be parallel to the street. In the interest of saving heating and cooling costs, this old standard may have to be abandoned. Actually, the slight angle required is of no significance and in most cases is not noticeable when shrubbery and other plantings are used. Fortunately, architects' files are full of designs for houses that look as good from one angle as another—that don't have to face any other direction than the one providing best exposure to solar energy.

Environment. This means simply, the location of a house—or the solar collector—so that it is not shaded by nearby trees or buildings. If you are building from scratch, the placement of the house on the lot can be influenced by the need for maximum exposure to the sun. If you are retrofitting, it may be worthwhile to remove growth that throws unwanted shadows. Remember, though, that the sun's angle changes over the course of a year. It's lower in winter and higher in summer. Also, southerly deciduous trees that provide cooling shade in summer will lose their leaves in autumn, allowing low-angle winter sunlight to reach solar collectors through the heating season.

In some localities it is unlawful for a neighbor to plant a tree or put up a building which would cast its shadow on your solar collector and interfere with its efficiency.

THE COST OF SOLAR HEAT. Solar energy is free. The only cost is the system required to collect the heat, store it when necessary, and deliver it where needed.

An ordinary fossil-fuel-burning furnace and the heat delivery system might cost less than $2,000. A solar heating system for the same home might cost much more. As great as this difference might seem, you must keep in mind that the cost of operating the solar heating system is so much less than the cost of ordinary fuels that the savings can make up the difference in just a few years. And, after those few years, the system holds good real estate value, should you ever sell the house.

In addition, many experts predict that the world will run out of petroleum by the year 2025. Other fossil fuels are also of limited quantity. When they are gone, what will be left? Solar heat.

Meanwhile, a consideration that should be of great importance to everyone is that a solar heated house causes no air pollution.

SOLAR LEGISLATION. While there are no regulations requiring the use of solar energy (as this is written), there are many legislative moves intended to augment the solar heat movement. In the works are bills aimed at reducing the cost of solar installation by making tax allowances or credits, by reduction in interest charges for money borrowed for solar installations, and by increased mortgage allowances to cover the cost of solar systems.

State laws differ widely, so it would be best to check with authorities in your home town to find out which, if any, offer incentives to go with solar collectors. Appendix I of this book offers a summary of recent incentives throughout North America. But you should also check with local authorities for any updates.

The figures on the map and the table on upcoming pages indicate average hours of sunshine by month and annually. For space heating, the figures during heating-season months are the vital ones. For domestic water heating, all months are considered to be significant.

MEAN MONTHLY TOTAL HOURS OF SUNSHINE

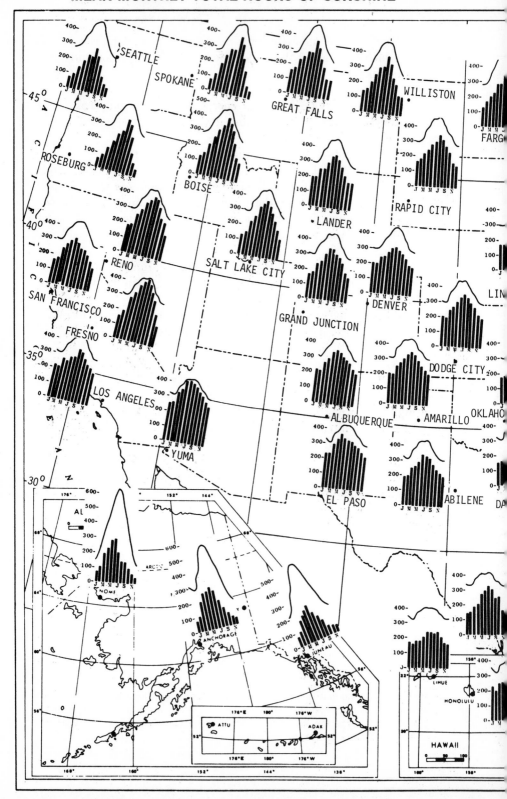

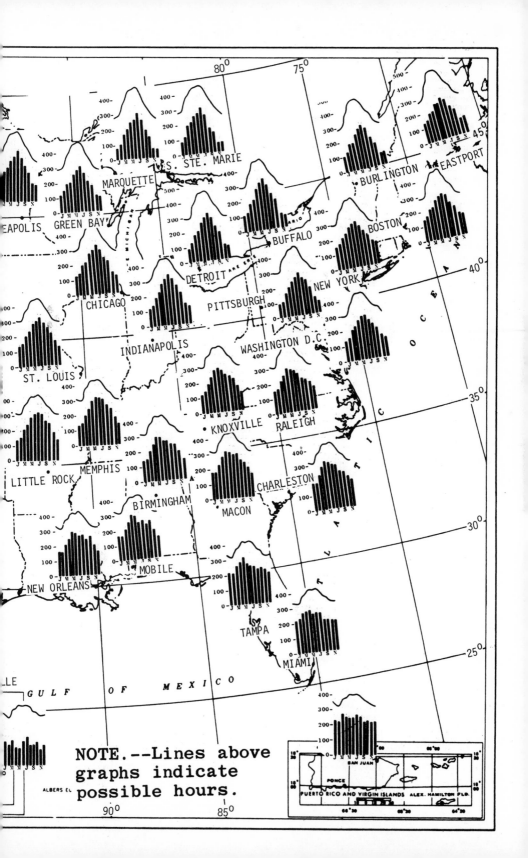

NOTE.--Lines above graphs indicate possible hours.

MEAN NUMBER OF HOURS OF SUNSHINE

STATE AND STATION	YRS.	JAN.	FEB.	MAR.	APR.	MAY	JUNE	JULY	AUG.	SEPT.	OCT.	NOV.	DEC.	ANNUAL
ALABAMA														
Birmingham	30	138	152	207	248	293	294	269	265	244	234	182	136	2662
Mobile	22	157	158	212	253	301	289	249	259	235	254	195	146	2708
Montgomery	30	160	168	227	267	317	311	288	290	260	250	200	156	2894
ALASKA														
Anchorage	19	78	114	210	254	268	288	255	184	128	96	68	49	1992
Fairbanks	20	54	120	224	302	319	334	274	164	122	85	71	36	2105
Juneau	29	71	102	171	200	230	251	193	161	123	67	60	51	1680
Nome	27	72	109	193	226	285	297	204	146	142	101	67	42	1884
ARIZONA														
Phoenix	30	248	244	314	346	404	404	377	351	334	307	267	236	3832
Prescott	14	222	230	293	323	378	392	323	305	315	286	254	228	3549
Tucson	13	255	266	317	350	399	394	329	329	335	317	280	258	3829
Yuma	30	258	266	337	365	419	420	404	380	351	330	285	262	4077
ARKANSAS														
Ft. Smith	30	146	156	202	234	268	303	321	305	261	230	174	147	2747
Little Rock	30	143	158	213	243	291	316	321	316	265	251	181	142	2840
CALIFORNIA														
Eureka	30	120	138	180	209	247	261	244	205	195	164	127	108	2198
Fresno	29	153	192	283	330	389	418	435	406	355	306	221	144	3632
Los Angeles	30	224	217	273	264	292	299	352	336	295	263	249	220	3284
Red Bluff	15	156	186	246	302	366	396	438	407	341	277	199	154	3468
Sacramento	30	134	169	255	300	367	405	437	406	347	283	197	122	3422
San Diego	30	216	212	262	242	261	253	293	277	255	234	236	217	2958
San Francisco	30	165	182	251	281	314	330	300	272	267	243	198	156	2959
COLORADO														
Denver	30	207	205	247	252	281	311	321	297	274	246	200	192	3033
Grand Junction	30	169	182	243	265	314	350	349	311	291	255	198	168	3095
Pueblo	30	224	217	261	271	299	340	349	318	290	265	225	211	3270
CONNECTICUT														
Hartford	30	141	166	206	223	267	285	299	268	220	193	137	136	2541
New Haven	30	155	178	215	234	274	291	309	284	238	215	157	154	2704
DIST. OF COLUMBIA														
Washington	30	138	160	205	226	267	288	291	264	233	207	162	135	2576

STATE AND STATION	YRS.	JAN.	FEB.	MAR.	APR.	MAY	JUNE	JULY	AUG.	SEPT.	OCT.	NOV.	DEC.	ANNUAL
FLORIDA														
Apalachicola	26	193	195	233	274	328	296	273	259	236	263	216	175	2941
Jacksonville	30	192	189	241	267	296	260	255	248	199	205	191	170	2713
Key West	30	229	238	285	296	307	273	277	269	236	237	226	225	3098
Lakeland	7	204	186	222	251	285	268	252	242	203	209	212	198	2732
Miami	30	222	227	266	275	280	251	267	263	216	215	212	209	2903
Pensacola	30	175	180	232	270	311	302	278	284	249	265	206	166	2918
Tampa	30	223	220	260	283	320	275	257	252	232	243	227	209	3001
GEORGIA														
Atlanta	25	154	165	218	266	309	304	284	285	247	241	188	160	2821
Macon	30	177	178	235	279	321	314	292	295	253	236	202	168	2950
Savannah	30	175	173	229	274	307	279	267	256	212	216	197	167	2752
HAWAII														
Hilo	7	153	135	161	112	106	158	184	134	137	153	106	131	1670
Honolulu	30	227	202	250	255	276	280	293	290	279	257	221	211	3041
Lihue	10	171	162	176	176	211	246	246	236	246	210	170	161	2411
IDAHO														
Boise	30	116	144	218	274	322	352	412	378	311	232	143	104	3006
Pocatello	30	111	143	211	255	300	338	380	347	296	230	145	108	2864
ILLINOIS														
Cairo	15	124	160	218	254	298	324	345	336	279	254	181	145	2918
Chicago	30	126	142	199	221	274	300	333	299	247	216	136	118	2611
Moline	18	132	139	189	214	255	279	337	300	251	214	130	123	2563
Peoria	30	134	149	198	229	273	303	336	299	259	222	149	122	2673
Springfield	30	127	149	193	224	282	304	346	312	266	225	152	122	2702
INDIANA														
Evansville	30	123	145	199	237	294	322	342	318	274	236	156	120	2766
Ft. Wayne	30	113	136	191	217	281	310	342	306	242	210	120	102	2570
Indianapolis	30	118	140	193	227	278	313	342	313	265	222	139	118	2668
Terre Haute	24	125	148	189	231	274	302	341	305	253	235	150	122	2675
IOWA														
Burlington	19	148	165	217	241	284	315	353	327	270	243	175	147	2885
Charles City	22	137	157	190	226	258	285	336	290	241	207	130	115	2572
Des Moines	30	155	170	203	236	276	303	346	299	263	227	156	136	2770
Sioux City	30	164	177	216	254	300	320	363	320	270	236	160	146	2926

(*continued*)

(MEAN NUMBER OF HOURS OF SUNSHINE Continued)

STATE AND STATION	YRS.	JAN.	FEB.	MAR.	APR.	MAY	JUNE	JULY	AUG.	SEPT.	OCT.	NOV.	DEC.	ANNUAL
KANSAS														
Concordia	30	180	172	214	243	281	315	348	308	249	245	189	172	2916
Dodge City	30	205	191	249	268	305	335	359	335	290	266	218	198	3219
Topeka	18	159	160	193	215	260	287	310	304	263	229	173	149	2702
Wichita	30	187	186	233	254	291	321	350	325	277	245	206	182	3057
KENTUCKY														
Louisville	30	115	135	188	221	283	303	324	295	256	219	148	114	2601
LOUISIANA														
New Orleans	30	160	158	213	247	292	287	260	269	241	260	200	157	2744
Shreveport	19	151	172	214	240	298	332	339	322	289	273	206	177	3015
MAINE														
Eastport	22	133	151	196	201	245	248	275	260	205	175	105	115	2309
Portland	30	155	174	213	226	268	286	312	294	229	202	146	148	2653
MARYLAND														
Baltimore	30	148	170	211	229	270	295	299	272	238	212	164	145	2653
MASSACHUSETTS														
Blue Hill Obs.	10	125	136	165	182	233	248	266	241	211	181	134	135	2257
Boston	30	148	168	212	222	263	283	300	280	232	207	152	148	2615
Nantucket	22	128	156	214	227	278	284	291	279	242	208	149	129	2585
MICHIGAN														
Alpena	24	86	124	198	228	261	303	339	285	204	159	70	67	2324
Detroit	30	90	128	180	212	263	295	321	284	226	189	98	89	2375
Lansing	30	84	119	175	215	272	305	344	294	228	182	87	73	2378
Escanaba	30	112	148	204	226	266	283	316	267	198	162	90	94	2366
Grand Rapids	30	74	117	178	218	277	308	349	304	231	188	92	70	2406
Marquette	30	78	113	172	207	248	268	305	251	186	142	68	66	2104
Sault Ste. Marie	30	83	123	187	217	252	269	309	256	165	133	61	62	2117
MINNESOTA														
Duluth	30	125	163	221	235	268	282	328	277	203	166	100	107	2475
Minneapolis	36	140	166	200	231	272	302	343	296	237	193	115	112	2607
MISSISSIPPI														
Jackson	12	130	147	199	244	280	287	279	287	235	223	185	150	2646
Vicksburg	30	136	141	199	232	284	304	291	297	254	244	183	140	2705

STATE AND STATION	YRS.	JAN.	FEB.	MAR.	APR.	MAY	JUNE	JULY	AUG.	SEPT.	OCT.	NOV.	DEC.	ANNUAL
MISSOURI														
Columbia	30	147	164	207	232	281	296	341	298	262	225	166	138	2757
Kansas City	30	154	170	211	235	278	313	347	308	266	235	178	151	2846
St. Joseph	23	154	165	211	231	274	301	347	287	260	224	168	144	2766
St. Louis	30	137	152	202	235	283	301	325	289	256	223	166	125	2694
Springfield	30	145	164	213	238	278	305	342	310	269	233	183	140	2820
MONTANA														
Billings	21	140	154	208	236	283	301	372	332	258	213	136	129	2762
Great Falls	19	154	176	245	261	299	299	381	342	256	206	132	133	2884
Havre	30	136	174	234	268	311	312	384	339	260	202	132	122	2874
Helena	30	138	168	215	241	292	292	342	336	258	202	137	121	2742
Missoula	25	85	109	167	209	261	260	378	328	246	178	90	66	2377
NEBRASKA														
Lincoln	30	173	172	213	244	287	316	356	309	266	237	174	160	2907
North Platte	30	181	179	221	246	282	310	343	304	264	242	184	169	2925
Omaha	30	172	188	222	259	305	332	379	311	270	248	166	145	2997
Valentine	30	185	194	229	252	296	323	369	326	275	242	174	172	3037
NEVADA														
Ely	22	186	197	262	260	300	354	359	344	303	255	204	187	3211
Las Vegas	8	239	251	314	336	386	411	383	364	345	301	258	250	3838
Reno	30	185	199	267	306	354	376	414	391	336	273	212	170	3483
Winnemucca	30	142	155	207	255	312	346	395	375	316	242	177	139	3061
NEW HAMPSHIRE														
Concord	23	136	153	192	196	229	261	286	260	214	179	122	126	2354
Mt. Wash. Obs.	18	94	98	133	141	162	145	150	143	139	159	89	87	1540
NEW JERSEY														
Atlantic City	30	151	173	210	233	273	287	298	271	239	218	177	153	2683
Trenton	30	145	168	203	235	277	294	309	273	239	208	160	142	2653
NEW MEXICO														
Albuquerque	30	221	218	273	299	343	365	340	317	299	279	245	219	3418
Roswell	21	218	223	286	306	330	333	341	313	266	266	242	216	3340
NEW YORK														
Albany	30	125	151	194	213	266	301	317	286	224	192	115	112	2496
Binghamton	30	94	119	151	170	226	256	266	230	184	158	92	79	2025
Buffalo	30	110	125	180	212	274	319	338	297	239	183	97	84	2458

(*continued*)

(MEAN NUMBER OF HOURS OF SUNSHINE Continued)

STATE AND STATION	YRS.	JAN.	FEB.	MAR.	APR.	MAY	JUNE	JULY	AUG.	SEPT.	OCT.	NOV.	DEC.	ANNUAL
New York	30	154	171	213	237	268	289	302	271	235	213	169	155	2677
Rochester	30	93	123	172	209	274	314	333	294	224	173	97	86	2392
Syracuse	30	87	115	165	197	261	295	316	276	211	163	81	74	2241
NORTH CAROLINA														
Asheville	30	146	161	211	247	289	292	268	250	235	222	179	146	2646
Cape Hatteras	9	152	168	206	259	293	301	286	265	214	202	169	154	2669
Charlotte	30	165	177	230	267	313	316	291	277	247	243	198	167	2891
Greensboro	30	157	171	217	231	298	302	287	272	243	236	190	163	2767
Raleigh	29	154	168	220	255	290	284	277	253	224	215	184	156	2680
Wilmington	30	179	180	237	279	314	312	286	273	237	238	206	178	2919
NORTH DAKOTA														
Bismarck	30	141	170	205	236	279	294	358	307	243	198	130	125	2686
Devils Lake	30	150	177	220	250	291	297	352	302	230	198	123	124	2714
Fargo	30	132	170	210	232	283	288	343	293	222	187	112	114	2586
Williston	29	141	168	215	260	305	312	377	328	247	206	131	129	2819
OHIO														
Cincinnati (ABBE)	30	115	137	186	222	273	309	323	295	253	205	138	118	2574
Cleveland	30	79	111	167	209	274	301	325	288	235	187	99	77	2352
Columbus	30	112	132	177	215	270	296	323	291	250	210	131	101	2508
Dayton	10	114	136	195	222	281	313	323	307	268	229	152	124	2664
Sandusky	30	100	128	183	229	285	312	343	302	248	201	111	91	2533
Toledo	30	93	120	170	203	263	296	331	298	241	196	106	92	2409
OKLAHOMA														
Oklahoma City	29	175	182	235	253	290	329	352	331	282	243	201	175	3048
Tulsa	18	152	164	200	213	244	287	314	308	281	241	207	172	2783
OREGON														
Baker	22	118	143	198	251	302	313	406	368	289	215	132	100	2835
Portland	30	77	97	142	203	246	249	329	275	218	134	87	65	2122
Roseburg	30	69	96	148	205	257	278	369	329	255	146	81	50	2283
PENNSYLVANIA														
Harrisburg	30	132	160	203	230	277	297	319	282	233	200	140	131	2604
Philadelphia	30	142	166	203	231	270	281	288	253	225	205	158	142	2564
Pittsburgh	25	89	114	163	200	239	260	283	250	234	180	114	76	2202
Reading	30	133	151	195	220	259	275	293	259	219	198	144	127	2473
Scranton	30	108	138	178	199	251	269	290	249	213	183	120	105	2303

STATE AND STATION	YRS.	JAN.	FEB.	MAR.	APR.	MAY	JUNE	JULY	AUG.	SEPT.	OCT.	NOV.	DEC.	ANNUAL
RHODE ISLAND														
Providence	30	145	168	211	221	271	285	292	267	226	207	153	143	2589
SOUTH CAROLINA														
Charleston	30	188	189	243	284	323	308	297	281	244	239	210	187	2993
Columbia	30	173	183	233	174	312	312	291	283	243	242	202	166	2914
Greenville	26	166	176	227	274	307	300	278	274	239	232	192	157	2822
SOUTH DAKOTA														
Huron	30	153	177	213	250	295	321	367	320	260	212	142	134	2844
Rapid City	30	164	182	222	245	278	300	348	317	266	228	164	144	2858
TENNESSEE														
Chattanooga	30	126	146	187	239	290	295	278	266	247	220	169	128	2591
Knoxville	30	124	144	189	237	281	288	277	248	237	213	157	120	2515
Memphis	30	135	152	204	244	296	321	319	314	261	243	180	139	2808
Nashville	30	123	142	196	241	285	308	292	279	250	224	168	126	2634
TEXAS														
Abilene	13	190	199	250	259	290	347	335	322	276	245	233	201	3137
Amarillo	30	207	199	258	276	305	338	350	328	288	260	229	205	3243
Austin	30	148	152	207	221	266	302	331	320	261	242	180	160	2790
Brownsville	30	147	152	187	210	272	297	326	311	246	252	165	151	2716
Corpus Christi	24	160	165	212	237	295	329	366	341	276	264	194	164	3003
Dallas	30	155	159	220	238	279	326	341	325	274	240	191	163	2911
Del Rio	27	173	173	230	237	259	279	331	319	252	240	195	178	2866
El Paso	30	234	236	299	329	373	369	336	327	300	287	257	236	3583
Galveston	30	151	149	203	230	288	322	305	292	257	264	199	151	2811
Houston	30	144	141	193	212	266	298	294	281	238	239	181	146	2633
Port Arthur	30	153	149	209	235	292	317	285	281	252	256	191	148	2768
San Antonio	30	148	153	214	224	258	292	325	307	261	241	183	160	2765
UTAH														
Salt Lake City	30	137	155	227	269	329	358	377	346	306	249	171	135	3059
VERMONT														
Burlington	30	103	127	184	185	244	270	291	266	199	152	77	80	2178
VIRGINIA														
Lynchburg	26	153	169	216	243	288	297	288	264	235	217	177	158	2705
Norfolk	30	156	174	223	257	304	311	296	282	237	220	182	161	2803
Richmond	30	144	166	211	248	280	296	286	263	230	211	176	152	2663

(*continued*)

(MEAN NUMBER OF HOURS OF   SUNSHINE Continued)

STATE AND STATION	YRS.	JAN.	FEB.	MAR.	APR.	MAY	JUNE	JULY	AUG.	SEPT.	OCT.	NOV.	DEC.	ANNUAL
WASHINGTON														
North Head	22	76	97	135	182	221	214	226	186	170	123	87	66	1783
Seattle	30	74	99	154	201	247	234	304	248	197	122	77	62	2019
Spokane	30	78	120	197	262	308	309	397	350	264	177	86	57	2605
Tatoosh Island	30	70	100	135	182	229	217	235	190	175	129	71	60	1793
Walla Walla	30	72	106	194	262	317	335	411	367	280	198	92	51	2685
WEST VIRGINIA														
Elkins	20	110	119	158	198	227	256	225	236	211	186	131	103	2160
Parkersburg	30	91	111	155	200	252	277	286	264	230	189	117	93	2265
WISCONSIN														
Green Bay	30	121	148	194	210	251	279	314	266	213	176	110	106	2388
Madison	30	126	147	196	214	258	285	336	288	230	198	116	106	2502
Milwaukee	30	116	134	191	218	267	293	340	292	235	193	125	106	2510
WYOMING														
Cheyenne	30	191	197	243	237	259	304	318	286	265	242	188	170	2900
Lander	30	200	208	260	264	301	340	361	326	280	233	186	185	3144
Sheridan	30	160	179	226	245	286	303	367	333	266	221	153	145	2884
PUERTO RICO														
San Juan	30	231	229	273	252	240	245	264	257	219	229	217	222	2878

HEATING DEGREE DAYS IN THE UNITED STATES

Heating degree days indicate the number of degrees the daily average temperatures are below 65°F. The figure 65° is used because it is the average outdoor temperature below which most people feel the need for indoor heat. Degree days are computed like this: A day with an average temperature of 50° has 15 heating degree days (65 − 50 = 15). Days that average 65° or over have no heating degree days.

This table shows the monthly and annual totals by city. Note: There is a direct relation between heating degree days and fuel consumption that allows fairly accurate comparisons of heating energy needs. For example, it would take roughly seven times as much energy to heat a house in Duluth as it would for the same house in New Orleans (10,000 ÷ 1385 = 7). And the relation of heating degree days to energy needs is fairly constant, whether any 100 degree days occur over many or only a few calendar days.

STATE AND STATION	JULY	AUG.	SEPT.	OCT.	NOV.	DEC.	JAN.	FEB.	MAR.	APR.	MAY	JUNE	ANNUAL
ALABAMA													
Birmingham	0	0	6	93	363	555	592	462	363	108	9	0	2551
Huntsville	0	0	12	127	426	663	694	557	434	138	19	0	3070
Mobile	0	0	0	22	213	357	415	300	211	42	0	0	1560
Montgomery	0	0	0	68	330	527	543	417	316	90	0	0	2291
ALASKA													
Anchorage	245	291	516	930	1284	1572	1631	1316	1293	879	592	315	10864
Annette	242	208	327	567	738	899	949	837	843	648	490	321	7069
Barrow	803	840	1035	1500	1971	2362	2517	2332	2468	1944	1445	957	20174
Barter Is.	735	775	987	1482	1944	2337	2536	2369	2477	1923	1373	924	19862
Bethel	319	394	612	1042	1434	1866	1903	1590	1655	1173	806	402	13196
Cold Bay	474	425	525	772	918	1122	1153	1036	1122	951	791	591	9880
Cordova	366	391	522	781	1017	1221	1299	1086	1113	864	660	444	9764
Fairbanks	171	332	642	1203	1833	2254	2359	1901	1739	1068	555	222	14279
Juneau	301	338	483	725	921	1135	1237	1070	1073	810	601	381	9075
King Salmon	313	322	513	908	1290	1606	1600	1333	1411	966	673	408	11343
Kotzebue	381	446	723	1249	1728	2127	2192	1932	2080	1554	1057	636	16105
McGrath	208	338	633	1184	1791	2232	2294	1817	1758	1122	648	258	14283
Nome	481	496	693	1094	1455	1820	1879	1666	1770	1314	930	573	14171
Saint Paul Is.	605	539	612	862	963	1197	1228	1168	1265	1098	936	726	11199
Shemya	577	475	501	784	876	1042	1045	958	1011	885	837	696	9687
Yakutat	338	347	474	716	936	1144	1169	1019	1042	840	632	435	9092
ARIZONA													
Flagstaff	46	68	201	558	867	1073	1169	991	911	651	437	180	7152
Phoenix	0	0	0	22	234	415	474	328	217	75	0	0	1765
Prescott	0	0	27	245	579	797	865	711	605	360	158	15	4362
Tucson	0	0	0	25	231	406	471	344	242	75	6	0	1800
Winslow	0	0	6	245	711	1008	1054	770	601	291	96	0	4782
Yuma	0	0	0	0	148	319	363	228	130	29	0	0	1217

(continued)

(HEATING-DEGREE-DAY TABLE Continued)

STATE AND STATION	JULY	AUG.	SEPT.	OCT.	NOV.	DEC.	JAN.	FEB.	MAR.	APR.	MAY	JUNE	ANNUAL
ARKANSAS													
Fort Smith	0	0	12	127	450	704	781	590	456	144	22	0	3292
Little Rock	0	0	9	127	465	716	756	577	434	126	9	0	3219
Texarkana	0	0	0	78	345	561	626	468	350	105	0	0	2533
CALIFORNIA													
Bakersfield	0	0	0	37	282	502	546	364	267	105	19	0	2122
Bishop	0	0	42	248	576	797	874	666	539	306	143	36	4227
Blue Canyon	34	50	120	347	579	766	865	781	791	582	397	195	5507
Burbank	0	0	6	43	177	301	366	277	239	138	81	18	1646
Eureka	270	257	258	329	414	499	546	470	505	438	372	285	4643
Fresno	0	0	0	78	339	558	586	406	319	150	56	0	2492
Long Beach	0	0	12	40	156	288	375	297	267	168	90	18	1711
Los Angeles	28	22	42	78	180	291	372	302	288	219	158	81	2061
Mt. Shasta	25	34	123	406	696	902	983	784	738	525	347	159	5722
Oakland	53	50	45	127	309	481	527	400	353	255	180	90	2870
Point Arguello	202	186	162	205	291	400	474	392	403	339	298	243	3595
Red Bluff	0	0	0	53	318	555	605	428	341	168	47	0	2515
Sacramento	0	0	12	81	363	577	614	442	360	216	102	6	2773
Sandberg	0	0	30	202	480	691	778	661	620	426	264	57	4209
San Diego	6	0	15	37	123	251	313	249	202	123	84	36	1439
San Francisco	81	78	60	143	306	462	508	395	363	279	214	126	3015
Santa Catalina	16	0	9	50	165	279	353	308	326	249	192	105	2052
Santa Maria	99	93	96	146	270	391	459	370	363	282	233	165	2967
COLORADO													
Alamosa	65	99	279	639	1065	1420	1476	1162	1020	696	440	168	8529
Colorado Springs	9	25	132	456	825	1032	1128	938	893	582	319	84	6423
Denver	6	9	117	428	819	1035	1132	938	887	558	288	66	6283
Grand Junction	0	0	30	313	786	1113	1209	907	729	387	146	21	5641
Pueblo	0	0	54	326	750	986	1085	871	772	429	174	15	5462
CONNECTICUT													
Bridgeport	0	0	66	307	615	986	1079	966	853	510	208	27	5617
Hartford	0	6	99	372	711	1119	1209	1061	899	495	177	24	6172
New Haven	0	12	87	347	648	1011	1097	991	871	543	245	45	5897
DELAWARE													
Wilmington	0	0	51	270	588	927	980	874	735	387	112	6	4930
FLORIDA													
Apalachicola	0	0	0	16	153	319	347	260	180	33	0	0	1308
Daytona Beach	0	0	0	0	75	211	248	190	140	15	0	0	879

STATE AND STATION	JULY	AUG.	SEPT.	OCT.	NOV.	DEC.	JAN.	FEB.	MAR.	APR.	MAY	JUNE	ANNUAL
Fort Myers	0	0	0	0	24	109	146	101	62	0	0	0	442
Jacksonville	0	0	0	12	144	310	332	246	174	21	0	0	1239
Key West	0	0	0	0	0	28	40	31	9	0	0	0	108
Lakeland	0	0	0	0	57	164	195	146	99	0	0	0	661
Miami Beach	0	0	0	0	0	40	56	36	9	0	0	0	141
Orlando	0	0	0	0	72	198	220	165	105	6	0	0	766
Pensacola	0	0	0	19	195	353	400	277	183	36	0	0	1463
Tallahassee	0	0	0	28	198	360	375	286	202	36	0	0	1485
Tampa	0	0	0	0	60	171	202	148	102	0	0	0	683
W. Palm Beach	0	0	0	0	6	65	87	64	31	0	0	0	253
GEORGIA													
Athens	0	0	12	115	405	632	642	529	431	141	22	0	2929
Atlanta	0	0	18	127	414	626	639	529	437	168	25	0	2983
Augusta	0	0	0	78	333	552	549	445	350	90	0	0	2397
Columbus	0	0	0	87	333	543	552	434	338	96	0	0	2383
Macon	0	0	0	71	297	502	505	403	295	63	0	0	2136
Rome	0	0	24	161	474	701	710	577	468	177	34	0	3326
Savannah	0	0	0	47	246	437	437	353	254	45	0	0	1819
Thomasville	0	0	0	25	198	366	394	305	208	33	0	0	1529
IDAHO													
Boise	0	0	132	415	792	1017	1113	854	722	438	245	81	5809
Idaho Falls 46W	16	34	270	623	1056	1370	1538	1249	1085	651	391	192	8475
Idaho Falls 42NW	16	40	282	648	1107	1432	1600	1291	1107	657	388	192	8760
Lewiston	0	0	123	403	756	933	1063	815	694	426	239	90	5542
Pocatello	0	0	172	493	900	1166	1324	1058	905	555	319	141	7033
ILLINOIS													
Cairo	0	0	36	164	513	791	856	680	539	195	47	0	3821
Chicago	0	0	81	326	753	1113	1209	1044	890	480	211	48	6155
Moline	0	9	99	335	774	1181	1314	1100	918	450	189	39	6408
Peoria	0	6	87	326	759	1113	1218	1025	849	426	183	33	6025
Rockford	6	9	114	400	837	1221	1333	1137	961	516	236	60	6830
Springfield	0	0	72	291	696	1023	1135	935	769	354	136	18	5429
INDIANA													
Evansville	0	0	66	220	606	896	955	767	620	237	68	0	4435
Fort Wayne	0	9	105	378	783	1135	1178	1028	890	471	189	39	6205
Indianapolis	0	0	90	316	723	1051	1113	949	809	432	177	39	5699
South Bend	0	6	111	372	777	1125	1221	1070	933	525	239	60	6439

(*continued*)

(HEATING-DEGREE-DAY TABLE Continued)

STATE AND STATION	JULY	AUG.	SEPT.	OCT.	NOV.	DEC.	JAN.	FEB.	MAR.	APR.	MAY	JUNE	ANNUAL
IOWA													
Burlington	0	0	93	322	768	1135	1259	1042	859	426	177	33	6114
Des Moines	0	9	99	363	837	1231	1398	1165	967	489	211	39	6808
Dubuque	12	31	156	450	906	1287	1420	1204	1026	546	260	78	7376
Sioux City	0	9	108	369	867	1240	1435	1198	989	483	214	39	6951
Waterloo	12	19	138	428	909	1296	1460	1221	1023	531	229	54	7320
KANSAS													
Concordia	0	0	57	276	705	1023	1163	935	781	372	149	18	5479
Dodge City	0	0	33	251	666	939	1051	840	719	354	124	9	4986
Goodland	0	6	81	381	810	1073	1166	955	884	507	236	42	6141
Topeka	0	0	57	270	672	980	1122	893	722	330	124	12	5182
Wichita	0	0	33	229	618	905	1023	804	645	270	87	6	4620
KENTUCKY													
Covington	0	0	75	291	669	983	1035	893	756	390	149	24	5265
Lexington	0	0	54	239	609	902	946	818	685	325	105	0	4683
Louisville	0	0	54	248	609	890	930	818	682	315	105	9	4660
LOUISIANA													
Alexandria	0	0	0	56	273	431	471	361	260	69	0	0	1921
Baton Rouge	0	0	0	31	216	369	409	294	208	33	0	0	1560
Burrwood	0	0	0	0	96	214	298	219	171	27	0	0	1024
Lake Charles	0	0	0	19	210	341	381	274	195	39	0	0	1459
New Orleans	0	0	0	19	192	322	363	258	192	39	0	0	1385
Shreveport	0	0	0	47	297	477	552	426	304	81	0	0	2184
MAINE													
Caribou	78	115	336	682	1044	1535	1690	1470	1308	858	468	183	9767
Portland	12	53	195	508	807	1215	1339	1182	1042	675	372	111	7511
MARYLAND													
Baltimore	0	0	48	264	585	905	936	820	679	327	90	0	4654
Frederick	0	0	66	307	624	955	995	876	741	384	127	12	5087
MASSACHUSETTS													
Blue Hill Obs.	0	22	108	381	690	1085	1178	1053	936	579	267	69	6368
Boston	0	9	60	316	603	983	1088	972	846	513	208	36	5634
Nantucket	12	22	93	332	573	896	992	941	896	621	384	129	5891
Pittsfield	25	59	219	524	831	1231	1339	1196	1063	660	326	105	7578
Worcester	6	34	147	450	774	1172	1271	1123	998	612	304	78	6969

STATE AND STATION	JULY	AUG.	SEPT.	OCT.	NOV.	DEC.	JAN.	FEB.	MAR.	APR.	MAY	JUNE	ANNUAL
MICHIGAN													
Alpena	68	105	273	580	912	1268	1404	1299	1218	777	446	156	8506
Detroit (City)	0	0	87	360	738	1088	1181	1058	936	522	220	42	6232
Escanaba	59	87	243	539	924	1293	1445	1296	1203	777	456	159	8481
Flint	16	40	159	465	843	1212	1330	1198	1066	639	319	90	7377
Grand Rapids	9	28	135	434	804	1147	1259	1134	1011	579	279	75	6894
Lansing	6	22	138	431	813	1163	1262	1142	1011	579	273	69	6909
Marquette	59	81	240	527	936	1268	1411	1268	1187	771	468	177	8393
Muskegon	12	28	120	400	762	1088	1209	1100	995	594	310	78	6696
Sault Ste. Marie	96	105	279	580	951	1367	1525	1380	1277	810	477	201	9048
MINNESOTA													
Duluth	71	109	330	632	1131	1581	1745	1518	1355	840	490	198	10000
Int. Falls	71	112	363	701	1236	1724	1919	1621	1414	828	443	174	10606
Minneapolis	22	31	189	505	1014	1454	1631	1380	1166	621	288	81	8382
Rochester	25	34	186	474	1005	1438	1593	1366	1150	630	301	93	8295
Saint Cloud	28	47	225	549	1065	1500	1702	1445	1221	666	326	105	8879
MISSISSIPPI													
Jackson	0	0	0	65	315	502	546	414	310	87	0	0	2239
Meridian	0	0	0	81	339	518	543	417	310	81	0	0	2289
Vicksburg	0	0	0	53	279	462	512	384	282	69	0	0	2041
MISSOURI													
Columbia	0	0	54	251	651	967	1076	874	716	324	121	12	5046
Kansas	0	0	39	220	612	905	1032	818	682	294	109	0	4711
St. Joseph	0	6	60	285	708	1039	1172	949	769	348	133	15	5484
St. Louis	0	0	60	251	627	936	1026	848	704	312	121	15	4900
Springfield	0	0	45	223	600	877	973	781	660	291	105	6	4561
MONTANA													
Billings	6	15	186	487	897	1135	1296	1100	970	570	285	102	7049
Glasgow	31	47	270	608	1104	1466	1711	1439	1187	648	335	150	8996
Great Falls	28	53	258	543	921	1169	1349	1154	1063	642	384	186	7750
Havre	28	53	306	595	1065	1367	1584	1364	1181	657	338	162	8700
Helena	31	59	294	601	1002	1265	1438	1170	1042	651	381	195	8129
Kalispell	50	99	321	654	1020	1240	1401	1134	1029	639	397	207	8191
Miles City	6	6	174	502	972	1296	1504	1252	1057	579	276	99	7723
Missoula	34	74	303	651	1035	1287	1420	1120	970	621	391	219	8125
NEBRASKA													
Grand Island	0	6	108	381	834	1172	1314	1089	908	462	211	45	6530

(*continued*)

(HEATING-DEGREE-DAY TABLE Continued)

STATE AND STATION	JULY	AUG.	SEPT.	OCT.	NOV.	DEC.	JAN.	FEB.	MAR.	APR.	MAY	JUNE	ANNUAL
Lincoln	0	6	75	301	726	1066	1237	1016	834	402	171	30	5864
Norfolk	9	0	111	397	873	1234	1414	1179	983	498	233	48	6979
North Platte	0	6	123	440	885	1166	1271	1039	930	519	248	57	6684
Omaha	0	12	105	357	828	1175	1355	1126	939	465	208	42	6612
Scotts Bluff	0	0	138	459	876	1128	1231	1008	921	552	285	75	6673
Valentine	9	12	165	493	942	1237	1395	1176	1045	579	288	84	7425
NEVADA													
Elko	9	34	225	561	924	1197	1314	1036	911	621	409	192	7433
Ely	28	43	234	592	939	1184	1308	1075	977	672	456	225	7733
Las Vegas	0	0	0	78	387	617	688	487	335	111	6	0	2709
Reno	43	87	204	490	801	1026	1073	823	729	510	350	189	6332
Winnemucca	0	34	210	536	876	1091	1172	916	837	573	363	153	6761
NEW HAMPSHIRE													
Concord	6	50	177	505	822	1240	1358	1184	1032	636	298	75	7383
Mt. Wash. Obs.	493	536	720	1057	1341	1742	1820	1663	1652	1260	930	603	13817
NEW JERSEY													
Atlantic City	0	0	39	251	549	880	936	848	741	420	133	15	4812
Newark	0	0	30	248	573	921	983	876	729	381	118	0	4859
Trenton	0	0	57	264	576	924	989	885	753	399	121	12	4980
NEW MEXICO													
Albuquerque	0	0	12	229	642	868	930	703	595	288	81	0	4348
Clayton	0	6	66	310	699	899	986	812	747	429	183	21	5158
Raton	9	28	126	431	825	1048	1116	904	834	543	301	63	6228
Roswell	0	0	18	202	573	806	840	641	481	201	31	0	3793
Silver City	0	0	6	183	525	729	791	605	518	261	87	0	3705
NEW YORK													
Albany	0	19	138	440	777	1194	1311	1156	992	564	239	45	6875
Binghamton (AP)	22	65	201	471	810	1184	1277	1154	1045	645	313	99	7286
Binghamton (PO)	0	28	141	406	732	1107	1190	1081	949	543	229	45	6451
Buffalo	19	37	141	440	777	1156	1256	1145	1039	645	329	78	7062
Central Park	0	0	30	233	540	902	986	885	760	408	118	9	4871
J. F. Kennedy Intl	0	0	36	248	564	933	1029	935	815	480	167	12	5219
Laguardia	0	0	27	223	528	887	973	879	750	414	124	6	4811
Rochester	9	31	126	415	747	1125	1234	1123	1014	597	279	48	6748
Schenectady	0	22	123	422	756	1159	1283	1131	970	543	211	30	6650
Syracuse	6	28	132	415	744	1153	1271	1140	1004	570	248	45	6756

STATE AND STATION	JULY	AUG.	SEPT.	OCT.	NOV.	DEC.	JAN.	FEB.	MAR.	APR.	MAY	JUNE	ANNUAL
NORTH CAROLINA													
Asheville	0	0	48	245	555	775	784	683	592	273	87	0	4042
Cape Hatteras	0	0	0	78	273	521	580	518	440	177	25	0	2612
Charlotte	0	0	6	124	438	691	691	582	481	156	22	0	3191
Greensboro	0	0	33	192	513	778	784	672	552	234	47	0	3805
Raleigh	0	0	21	164	450	716	725	616	487	180	34	0	3393
Wilmington	0	0	0	74	291	521	546	462	357	96	0	0	2347
Winston Salem	0	0	21	171	483	747	753	652	524	207	37	0	3595
NORTH DAKOTA													
Bismarck	34	28	222	577	1083	1463	1708	1442	1203	645	329	117	8851
Devils Lake	40	53	273	642	1191	1634	1872	1579	1345	753	381	138	9901
Fargo	28	37	219	574	1107	1569	1789	1520	1262	690	332	99	9226
Williston	31	43	261	601	1122	1513	1758	1473	1262	681	357	141	9243
OHIO													
Akron	0	9	96	381	726	1070	1138	1016	871	489	202	39	6037
Cincinnati	0	0	54	248	612	921	970	837	701	336	118	9	4806
Cleveland	9	25	105	384	738	1088	1159	1047	918	552	260	66	6351
Columbus	0	6	84	347	714	1039	1088	949	809	426	171	27	5660
Dayton	0	6	78	310	696	1045	1097	955	809	429	167	30	5622
Mansfield	9	22	114	397	768	1110	1169	1042	924	543	245	60	6403
Sandusky	0	6	66	313	684	1032	1107	991	868	495	198	36	5796
Toledo	0	16	117	406	792	1138	1200	1056	924	543	242	60	6494
Youngstown	6	19	120	412	771	1104	1169	1047	921	540	248	60	6417
OKLAHOMA													
Oklahoma City	0	0	15	164	498	766	868	664	527	189	34	0	3725
Tulsa	0	0	18	158	522	787	893	683	539	213	47	0	3860
OREGON													
Astoria	146	130	210	375	561	679	753	622	636	480	363	231	5186
Burns	12	37	210	515	867	1113	1246	988	856	570	366	177	6957
Eugene	34	34	129	366	585	719	803	627	589	426	279	135	4726
Meacham	84	124	288	580	918	1091	1209	1005	983	726	527	339	7874
Medford	0	0	78	372	678	871	918	697	642	432	242	78	5008
Pendleton	0	0	111	350	711	884	1017	773	617	396	205	63	5127
Portland	25	28	114	335	597	735	825	644	586	396	245	105	4635
Roseburg	22	16	105	329	567	713	766	608	570	405	267	123	4491
Salem	37	31	111	338	594	729	822	647	611	417	273	144	4754
Sexton Summit	81	81	171	443	666	874	958	809	818	609	465	279	6254

(*continued*)

(HEATING-DEGREE-DAY TABLE Continued)

STATE AND STATION	JULY	AUG.	SEPT.	OCT.	NOV.	DEC.	JAN.	FEB.	MAR.	APR.	MAY	JUNE	ANNUAL
PENNSYLVANIA													
Allentown	0	0	90	353	693	1045	1116	1002	849	471	167	24	5810
Erie	0	25	102	391	714	1063	1169	1081	973	585	288	60	6451
Harrisburg	0	0	63	298	648	992	1045	907	766	396	124	12	5251
Philadelphia	0	0	60	291	621	964	1014	890	744	390	115	12	5101
Pittsburgh	0	9	105	375	726	1063	1119	1002	874	480	195	39	5987
Scranton	0	19	132	434	762	1104	1156	1028	893	498	195	33	6254
Williamsport	0	9	111	375	717	1073	1122	1002	856	468	177	24	5934
RHODE ISLAND													
Block Is.	0	16	78	307	594	902	1020	955	877	612	344	99	5804
Providence	0	16	96	372	660	1023	1110	988	868	534	236	51	5954
SOUTH CAROLINA													
Charleston	0	0	0	59	282	471	487	389	291	54	0	0	2033
Columbia	0	0	0	84	345	577	570	470	357	81	0	0	2484
Florence	0	0	0	78	315	552	552	459	347	84	0	0	2387
Greenville	0	0	0	112	387	636	648	535	434	120	12	0	2884
Spartanburg	0	0	15	130	417	667	663	560	453	144	25	0	3074
SOUTH DAKOTA													
Huron	9	12	165	508	1014	1432	1628	1355	1125	600	288	87	8223
Rapid City	22	12	165	481	897	1172	1333	1145	1051	615	326	126	7345
Sioux Falls	19	25	168	462	972	1361	1544	1285	1082	573	270	78	7839
TENNESSEE													
Bristol	0	0	51	236	573	828	828	700	598	261	68	0	4143
Knoxville	0	0	30	171	489	725	732	613	493	198	43	0	3494
Memphis	0	0	18	130	447	698	729	585	456	147	22	0	3232
Nashville	0	0	30	158	495	732	778	644	512	189	40	0	3578
Oak Ridge (CO)	0	0	39	192	531	772	778	669	552	228	56	0	3817
TEXAS													
Amarillo	0	0	18	205	570	797	877	664	546	252	56	0	3985
Austin	0	0	0	31	225	388	468	325	223	51	0	0	1711
Corpus Christi	0	0	0	0	120	220	291	174	109	0	0	0	914
Dallas	0	0	0	62	321	524	601	440	319	90	6	0	2363
El Paso	0	0	0	84	414	648	685	445	319	105	0	0	2700
Fort Worth	0	0	0	65	324	536	614	448	319	99	0	0	2405
Galveston	0	0	0	0	138	270	350	258	189	30	0	0	1235
Houston	0	0	0	6	183	307	384	288	192	36	0	0	1396
Midland	0	0	0	87	381	592	651	468	322	90	0	0	2591
San Antonio	0	0	0	31	207	363	428	286	195	39	0	0	1549

STATE AND STATION	JULY	AUG.	SEPT.	OCT.	NOV.	DEC.	JAN.	FEB.	MAR.	APR.	MAY	JUNE	ANNUAL
Victoria	0	0	0	6	150	270	344	230	152	21	0	0	1173
Waco	0	0	0	43	270	456	536	389	270	66	0	0	2030
Wichita Falls	0	0	0	99	381	632	698	518	378	120	6	0	2832
UTAH													
Milford	0	0	99	443	867	1141	1252	988	822	519	279	87	6497
Salt Lake City	0	0	81	419	849	1082	1172	910	763	459	233	84	6052
Wendover	0	0	48	372	822	1091	1178	902	729	408	177	51	5778
VERMONT													
Burlington	28	65	207	539	891	1349	1513	1333	1187	714	353	90	8269
VIRGINIA													
Cape Henry	0	0	0	112	360	645	694	633	536	246	53	0	3279
Lynchburg	0	0	51	223	540	822	849	731	605	267	78	0	4166
Norfolk	0	0	0	136	408	698	738	655	533	216	37	0	3421
Richmond	0	0	36	214	495	784	815	703	546	219	53	0	3865
Roanoke	0	0	51	229	549	825	834	722	614	261	65	0	4150
WASHINGTON													
Olympia	68	71	198	422	636	753	834	675	645	450	307	177	5236
Seattle	50	47	129	329	543	657	738	599	577	396	242	117	4424
Seattle Tacoma	56	62	162	391	633	750	828	678	657	474	295	159	5145
Spokane	9	25	168	493	879	1082	1231	980	834	531	288	135	6655
Stampede Pass	273	291	393	701	1008	1178	1287	1075	1085	855	654	483	9283
Walla Walla	0	0	87	310	681	843	986	745	589	342	177	45	4805
Yakima	0	12	144	450	828	1039	1163	868	713	435	220	69	5941
WEST VIRGINIA													
Charleston	0	0	63	254	591	865	880	770	648	300	96	9	4476
Elkins	9	25	135	400	729	992	1008	896	791	444	198	48	5675
Parkersburg	0	0	60	264	606	905	942	826	691	339	115	6	4754
WISCONSIN													
Green Bay	28	50	174	484	924	1333	1494	1313	1141	654	335	99	8029
La Crosse	12	19	153	437	924	1339	1504	1277	1070	540	245	69	7589
Madison	25	40	174	474	930	1330	1473	1274	1113	618	310	102	7863
Milwaukee	43	47	174	471	876	1252	1376	1193	1054	642	372	135	7635
WYOMING													
Casper	6	16	192	524	942	1169	1290	1084	1020	657	381	129	7410
Cheyenne	19	31	210	543	924	1101	1228	1056	1011	672	381	102	7278
Lander	6	19	204	555	1020	1299	1417	1145	1017	654	381	153	7870
Sheridan	25	31	219	539	948	1200	1355	1154	1054	642	366	150	7683

2 | Basics of Solar Heating and Cooling

EVEN IF YOU INTEND to hire a contractor to do your solar heating and cooling installation, it is of interest and importance that you understand how basic systems work. This will help you make vital decisions as to the kind of system you want, and it will help you to keep your system operating at top efficiency.

Basically, a solar heating system consists of the following elements:
- A *collector* that converts the sun's rays into heat
- A *delivery system* that sends the heat where it is needed
- *Storage facilities* that hold required heat during sunless periods
- A *backup system* that can compensate for insufficient sunshine
- A *heat exchanger* that puts the heat to work. (In addition, there may be need for controls to modify the amount of heating for maximum efficiency.)

SOLAR COLLECTORS. There are dozens of types of solar-heat collectors, but they all function with variations of the same principle: the absorption of infrared heat rays given off by the sun. This absorption is greatest when the sun's rays strike a black surface—one that is dull, not glossy. This black surface is almost always metal. When the flat-black surface is placed at right angles to the rays of the sun, a tremendous amount of heat is absorbed by the metal. In fact, so much heat is absorbed that one of the basic problems in solar heat is drawing that heat into the delivery system before things get dangerously hot.

To prevent unwanted overheating of the surrounding structure of the system and to prevent heat loss, standard collectors are insulated. Some highly mechanical systems are equipped with blinds of one sort or another, which close automatically to cut off the sunlight when a certain temperature is reached.

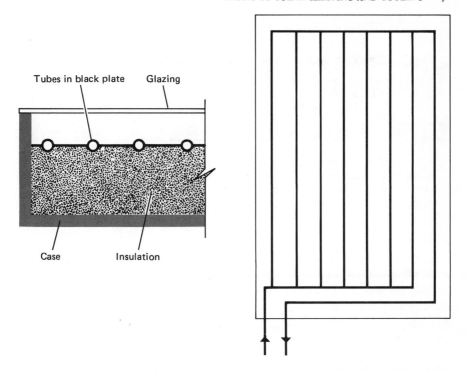

These drawings show the basic structure of the solar collector using a liquid. The tubes, bonded to the black plate, pick up the heat and transfer it to the liquid. The tubes are laid out in a pattern that allows the liquid to flow in, across the black plate, and out of the collector into service, thereby heating space or water.

To prevent heat loss to the atmosphere, collectors have a glass or plastic cover. The infrared rays from the sun pass through this clear material and the resultant heat is trapped.

The collector surface may be smooth or corrugated, or channeled in one way or another, depending on engineering. A collector based on a flat plate is simple to make, and is the favorite of the do-it-yourselfer.

In addition, some heat collectors consist of tubes, channels, or other forms that are black on the outside and conduct the heat into the hollow centers for transmission to the delivery system.

The heat collector incorporates some method of transferring the collected heat to the delivery system. The transfer medium may be a liquid, such as water, or a gas, such as air. When the medium is a liquid, the collector usually has tubes that are bonded to the black collecting surface. To use air as a medium, the collector is engineered with ducts of one form or another through which the air flows, picking up heat as it goes. This form

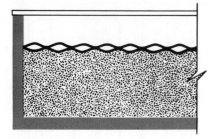 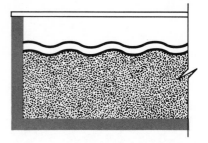

Heat collectors using air as the delivery medium usually incorporate ducting similar to these two options. Corrugated sheets may be fastened together (left) to form channels for the air to move through. Or, they may be spaced (right) so that the heated air flows between the sheets.

of collector is most commonly used when the objective is to feed a warm-air heating system, since it doesn't require a heat exchanger.

The fundamental design of heat collectors is shown in the accompanying drawings. Commercially and industrially, they are available in units which can be combined to produce the total collector area required for the specific situation.

DELIVERY SYSTEMS. Solar heating systems which use warm-air usually utilize standard duct work throughout the house. The same type of fan used to move the air in a standard warm-air system pushes warmed air through the system, and recirculates it through the collector for reheating.

There are also warm-air systems which do not call upon a fan, but utilize convection as the moving force. Warm air rises, cool air descends. These convection systems are effective except in homes where the heating demand is relatively high and convection movement of air is not rapid enough.

Another heat-delivery method used in some warm-air installations uses no duct work. The heat is collected on the sunny side of the house and—figuratively speaking—is delivered through the backside of the collector into the living area. This is similar to the way the sun delivers heat into the house through ordinary south-oriented windows.

When a liquid is the delivery medium, some sort of circulating system is usually required. Convection can be used in rare situations, but most frequently liquid must be circulated faster than natural convection flow.

The pumps that circulate the water do not have to be big or expensive, since there is relatively little resistance to the movement of the liquid. Water seeks its own level, and therefore all the pump does is provide enough circulation to ensure that the temperature is high enough at the heat exchanger or radiator.

One of the problems with liquid delivery systems is the danger of freezing in cold weather. This occurs when the call for heat is off and the liquid may be standing in the collector tubes in the cold. In some systems, freeze-ups are avoided by means of controls that drain the water from the collector when the temperature is low. Another precaution is the use of an antifreeze in the water. This, of course, will not work in a system that heats water directly for kitchen and bath use. In this case, a heat exchanger must be used to heat water that comes in from the supply lines.

One of the solar collectors made commercially uses a *black* liquid, in transparent tubes, to increase the absorption of the sun's rays.

Storage tanks. As long as the sun is shining, there is little need for storage. But the sun sets every evening. And sometimes it will hide behind clouds for days on end. To keep solar-heating systems from going dead at night or during adverse weather, a storage tank is used.

For water-transported solar heat, the storage tank is just a big, insulated tank. Water heated during the sun's working hours is in constant circulation through the tank. Eventually, all the water in the tank is heated. When the sun goes down, this heated water supplies the required heat. Gradually the water cools, but when the sun shines again, reheating begins. A proper-size tank will generally hold enough heat to take care of things for up to five sunless days. (Still, the sun's rays make their way through thin clouds. The resultant rays are weak, but it takes really cloudy skies to shut the rays off completely.)

The storage tank for hot-air systems sounds almost primitive. It usually consists of a large *bin of rocks,* through which the heated air circulates. The

Collection of heat in roof-mounted bags of water is the innovation of Harold Hay and Sky Therm. The bags, 8 inches thick, absorb heat and transmit it through the ceiling into living quarters. At night, insulation slides over the bags, preventing the loss of heat into the cool nighttime air. During warm seasons, the shutters are closed by day and opened at night. The bags are cooled by night air and help cool the house during the day.

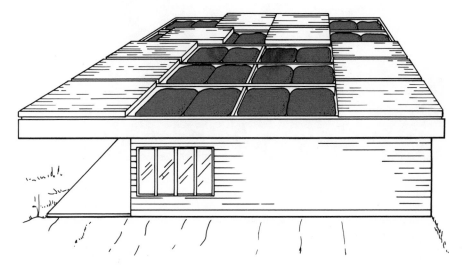

rocks become hot and hold the heat until it is needed. When the sun is no longer providing warmth directly, the air circulating through the rock bin picks up heat from the rocks. See Chapter 11 for a description and drawing showing how to build a hot-air storage tank.

BACKUP SYSTEMS. It is a rare solar-heating system that can count on the sun for absolutely all heating needs at all times. A system that supplied all your home heating needs in the coldest months of the year would be loafing along and wasting a lot of its potential for the balance of the year. That would make a solar heating system that supplies 100 percent of your heat a very poor investment. For that reason, systems are usually linked up with electric-resistance heating or with an oil- or gas-burning furnace that comes on when the solar collector can't handle the whole job. Thermostatic controls make 'the backup automatic.

It is also a common practice to back up the solar-heating system with a wood-burning stove. Many small stoves that were the only source of heat in many living rooms a few decades ago are again on the market to back up solar heating and also to reduce consumption of gas and oil.

HEAT EXCHANGERS. The function of the heat exchanger is to take the heat from the collector-delivery combination and translate it into usable

Shown here is a recent development called Sunwall, by Kalwall Corporation. This Sunwall unit is mounted on an addition to a farmhouse. Sunwall involves two sheets of fiberglass about 2¾ inches apart. Tiny foam beads by Zomeworks Beadwall are blown into the space during the night, for insulation, then sucked out during the day to let heat in.

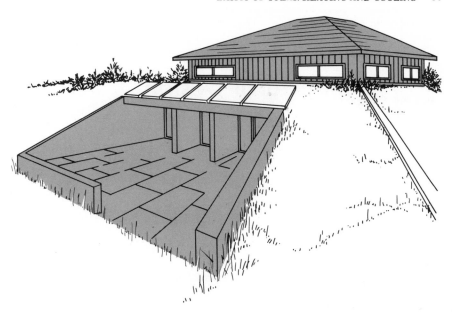

Earth berming is a great heat saver, cutting heat loss almost to zero through the lower part of the walls backed up by earth built up to window height. As shown here, the berm may provide support for the solar collectors.

heat. For example, the exchanger would be immersed in a tank of water in the household water system, giving off its heat to the water. In this situation the exchanger could be simply a spiral of tubing.

When heated water is used to provide warm air, the exchanger takes the form of a finned tube or chamber. The water delivers heat through the fins, and the heat is absorbed by moving air.

All of the foregoing methods and materials are available from commercial solar-heat suppliers. Also, many of the systems are simple enough to make yourself. The key is to make sure a given system will meet your requirements.

3 The Importance of Architectural Design

WHETHER YOU ARE THINKING about putting solar heat to work in your present home or whether you are planning a new house, architecture should be a primary consideration.

Many existing dwellings can be retrofitted with solar heat quickly and easily. Others may require modification. On the other hand, it makes little sense to build a new home without considering solar energy as a *prime* design factor.

Few people realize that the problem of heating and cooling has long been a strong influence on house design. The traditional Cape Cod, with its low walls and small roof area, could be kept livable in winter with an ordinary wood stove. The saltbox design, with the south wall two stories high and the north wall only one story, allowed the higher wall to absorb heat from the sun. Meanwhile, the long-slanting north roof fended off the cold northerly winds.

Today, both the saltbox and the Cape Cod can be easily equipped for solar heating because the roof conditions are right. Either pitch of the Cape

A   B

Two classic roof designs: (A) the saltbox, and (B) the Cape Cod.

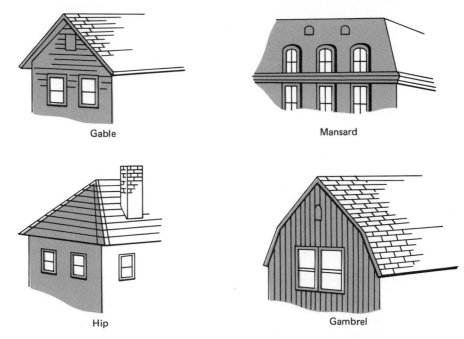

Gable   Mansard

Hip   Gambrel

The four most common roof types in existing homes are shown here. The gable is
the most used of all styles. All of these roofs can be used for solar-heat collection.

Cod roof represents about one-half of the floor area, which is normally
more than enough for the size of the collector panels required. (Both designs also lend themselves to modernization, as discussed later in this
chapter.)

Many of the so-called "conservative modern" homes built in recent years
—such as the ranch house—are also well suited for solar conversion, provided
there is a roof facing south.

However, the traditional hip roof does not usually provide enough area,
even though one of its four roof pitches is almost certain to face south. The
classic mansard usually supports windowed dormers that would interfere.
The gambrel roof, with its double-angle pitch might provide an extra advantage with a collector angled over both pitches. The more vertical section would catch the morning and afternoon sun, while the more horizontal
section would work best at midday.

The mansard must not be counted out entirely. The flat top of the roof
could be a good location for a collector made of several units supported
at the proper angle—facing the proper direction—none of them conspicuous
from the street.

Meanwhile, a large share of the 70-million homes in the U.S. today could

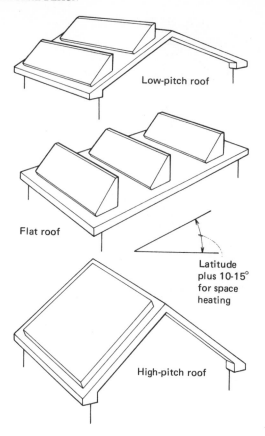

Solar collectors can be installed on almost any roof situation, if you follow the "latitude" formula. The pitch of the collector should be the latitude of your area plus or minus 10 degrees.

Low-pitch roof

Flat roof

Latitude plus 10-15° for space heating

High-pitch roof

easily be retrofitted with sufficient solar facilities to handle *domestic water* needs. And a great many could undergo required modifications to make solar heating and cooling possible.

ARCHITECTURAL UPDATES. Some of the best modern solar-home designs are little more than variations on traditional designs. The accompanying photographs illustrate examples.

The Acorn. This house is very close to Cape Cod in basic design, although there are some features of particular interest:

• First, there are fewer windows than the traditional design would have. The reason for this is the need for cutting down heat loss in the winter and heat gain in the summer.

• Note the degree of overhang at the eaves. This overhang shades the windows in summer, when the sun is high, and while the solar energy system in the house is providing air conditioning. In the winter, when the sun is lower, the sun can shine through the windows to help with the heating.

The resemblance of this modern Acorn-built home to the old Cape Cod is evident. This update was designed basically to accept solar heat. This efficient collector shown absorbs enough for home heating even though it covers only about half of one roof pitch.

- Trees are kept away from the southern exposure of the house, where their shadows would reduce solar accumulation. But they are close and tall in back of the house, acting as a windbreak to cut down on heating needs.
- The standard chimney is there, indicating that some sort of fuel burner is available as a backup.

A Richard Crowther house. The two photographs show the front and back of a house designed by Richard Crowther, echoing the old saltbox design. Some of the heating and cooling features of the saltbox are used, as well.

- The solar collector is on the steeper of the two roof areas, and it is pitched to take the greatest advantage of sunlight in the locality.
- The northerly, flatter roof is angled to deflect icy winds, just as the traditional saltbox does.
- Note the relatively few windows and the overhang that protects them from the sun in summer while exposing them in winter.
- The chimney, along an outside wall, is of contemporary design. It indicates that backup heating is available. Note also the vent at the roof peak.
- An especially useful feature is the location of the garage on the cold side of the house, providing an excellent insulating service.
- Note that the trees on the south side of the house are far enough away so that their shadows do not hit the solar collector.

The saltbox design is carried over in this house, designed by Richard Crowther for Solaron. The angle of the southern-exposed roof is determined by latitude, which determines the sun's angle.

SOLAR-INSPIRED ARCHITECTURE. Despite the increase in retrofitted solar homes and the adaptations of classic architectural designs, the most significant moves have been toward houses specifically designed to take the greatest advantage of solar heating and cooling. Many architects as well as producers of solar heating equipment have gone to the drawing board with one primary objective: to design a house that the sun will heat and cool most effectively and economically.

This is the "Solar One" house, said to be the first house designed to convert sun-light into both heat and electricity. Maximum roof exposure is made possible by the single-pitch, angled and oriented for maximum absorption.

Roofs. The influence shows most, of course, in roofs. The pitch is dictated by the latitude where the house is built, and is angled to take fullest advantage of sun rays. The size is dictated by the area required for the solar collector, and this produces two design changes:

• The single-pitch roof is steeper. Single-pitch once was used mainly for nearly flat roofs. Solar design calls for a roof that has only one surface, but that surface is angled to best catch the sun. When the roof rises from a single-story height in front to a two-story height in back, the result is a large roof area.

• Roofs may be extended beyond their normal overhang. This extension is used to provide larger area when needed, along with the required overhang to prevent unwanted entry by the sun's rays. Another method of in-

The Acorn garage is intended for use in situations where the house cannot be counted on to support the solar collector. This is a complete free-standing unit.

This Solaron house, specifically designed for utilization of solar energy, demonstrates that a solar collector mounted on the front of a house need not be an eyesore. The garage roof can accommodate more collector area, in the event the living space is expanded.

Mounted on the back of the house, this collector by Revere Copper & Brass, spreads over a large roof area, to provide energy for a house with several rooms downstairs and up.

creasing the area of roof collectors is "teaming up" the residential roof with an adjoining garage or other utility building.

Windows. The solar-heated home takes advantage of window placement that brings heat in. In this case, there is a minimum of windows on the "cold" sides of the house.

Auxiliary elements. In situations where proper orientation of the entire house is not feasible, architects work out eye-pleasing wings, porches, garages, or other elements which can be built facing the proper direction.

STRUCTURAL CHANGES FOR SOLAR HEAT.

Insulation is a vital factor in residential construction planned for solar heating. Quite simply, reducing the heat loss cuts down the heating requirements, thus making it possible for a well-engineered solar heating system to fulfill the needs of the entire house with little or no help from backup installations.

More efficient insulating materials are being used, and they are used in increased thicknesses. Other building materials are selected as much for their low heat-transmission characteristics as for their structural strength.

Solar-based architecture in some instances reduces the amount of the house exposed to the climate by raising the ground level. In some cases, the earth may be bermed to reach the eave line, taking advantage of the in-

This is a model of a prefab house, engineered for easy on-site assembly by a contractor or the homeowner himself, included is the solar package, priced at about $4,000, if installed by the homeowner. (Architect, Donald Watson)

This smaller home, developed by Solar Homes, Inc., takes advantage of the attached garage to achieve sufficient roof space for the collector, which stretches the length of the building. Note the window-shading overhang.

For this low-roof ranch-type house, solar collector units from Revere are mounted on the ground.

The roof of the main part of this house was unsuitably angled and oriented. So the collector was mounted on the roof of an addition, oriented the other way. The job was done by Southeastern Solar Systems, in Georgia.

sulating value of soil and plantings. The ultimate in the use of soil as a barrier to heat loss is the house with a sod-covered roof.

When all of these methods of heat conservation are used, it may be possible to heat the home with a solar collector no larger than 10 to 30 percent of the home's floor space.

With the growing degree of interest in solar heating among today's architects, you will have no trouble finding an architect in your area who has already worked out solutions for the problems that apply to your situation. Talk to two or three architects, to find the one whose overall thinking seems to make the most sense.

The extra-strength piling on the front of this house helps support the 18-inches of soil and sod acting as insulation on the back pitch. Collectors are the Thomason "trickle-down" design.

A small, aluminum type solar collector serves this home for domestic water needs. Installation is simple and inexpensive in retrofitting situations, where use of solar energy for total heating needs is not feasible.

Roof slopes in this housing development are just what the architect wanted. But the garage roof is deliberately slanted for maximum collection of solar energy. Garages and additions often present this opportunity, both in new homes and old.

The roof angles on this house are uniform and correspond with the overall architecture—except for the roof deliberately elevated and pitched for solar efficiency.

4 | Passive Solar System — Simplest of All

PASSIVE SOLAR HEATING SYSTEMS take advantage of solar heat without any mechanical components—that is, without any transmission facilities as such. For that reason, passive systems tend to be low in cost, require little or no energy for normal operation, and present virtually no maintenance problems.

On the other hand, their production of heat from solar energy may be lower and may take place more slowly than that available through well-designed active systems. For that reason, backup from regular fuel-burning systems is usually necessary, except in relatively mild climates that are rich with sunlight.

In simple terms, passive solar heating draws heat into the building and distributes it basically through natural convection and radiation. (In some situations, a small electric fan may be needed to boost movement; when this is true, the system is called a "hybrid.")

Storage of the heat takes place in the walls, floors, ceilings, and contents of the house. Sometimes storage is augmented by means of heat-absorbing elements inside the house. These can be as rudimentary as an attic full of gallon bottles, filled with water. In fact, water beds have been used for heat storage. Somewhat more sophisticated are vertical, tubular tanks of water, placed just inside the solar-heat inlets.

In design and construction of passive systems, extreme care is taken to let the maximum amount of sunlight enter but to insulate heavily against heat loss when there is no sun. The systems operate most efficiently when the house has the maximum possible insulation, even on the outside of concrete basement walls and beneath concrete basement floors. This insulation does more than cut down on ordinary heat loss. It also improves the excellent heat-storage capacities of concrete masonry, which in some homes is poured extra thick to provide extra storage capacity.

TYPES OF HEAT-GAIN SYSTEMS. There are three types of heat-gain systems in use today.

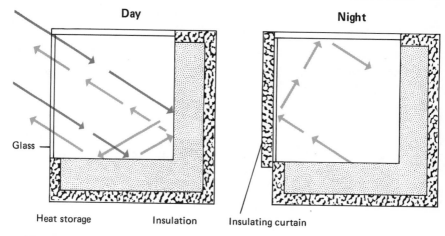

The principle of direct-gain heating is shown in these drawings. At left, sunlight enters the window and heats the walls and floors of the room, which store the heat. When the insulating curtain is drawn at night (right) the walls and floors release the heat to the house.

Direct gain. The heat enters the living area through windows or window-like collectors. As it spreads throughout the area, it transmits its heat to the surroundings, which store the heat. When the sun sets and the temperature of the air in the room starts to drop, the storage masses start releasing heat.

The main shortcoming of the direct-gain system is that living areas may become too hot for comfort, in order to serve their heat storage function. This usually calls for careful control of the heat gain by means of insulation or blinds. Another means of control is to make construction *massive* so that there is plenty of material to absorb heat. Also, there are building materials under development that can store a great deal of heat without overheating the living space. These look promising.

Indirect gain. Heat from the sun is picked up by a heat-storage unit of one sort or another, from which it is released to the living area, as needed. The collectors are often situated in the living area and designed to serve as part of the decor—not part of a heating system. See the accompanying drawings.

Isolated gain. This system involves storage-collector components which are separated from the living area. However, their relationship to living areas is such that they can transmit their heat as needed, through radiation or convection. These systems are the ones most frequently aided by some sort of air-moving equipment and are thus called hybrids.

HEAT-GATHERING FACILITIES. South-facing windows are the simplest and most common means of passive heat gain. When these windows are

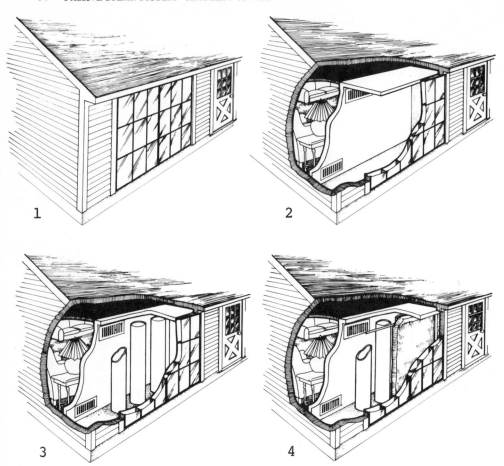

The principle of indirect gain is illustrated in the above drawings from Kalwall. Solar heat enters through the collector (1), into an insulated enclosure (2). Inside this enclosure are storage tanks which hold the heat. Air circulates through the enclosure through registers (3). When the sun is not shining, an insulating shield is drawn between the glazing and the heat storage tanks.

Well within do-it-yourself range is the Drum-Wall system on the next page (by solar-heat innovator Steve Baer). Water in a rack of 55-gallon oil drums stores the heat, which is collected when sun rays hit the black-painted barrels. A hinged, insulated shutter outside is opened and closed by means of a rope and pulley.

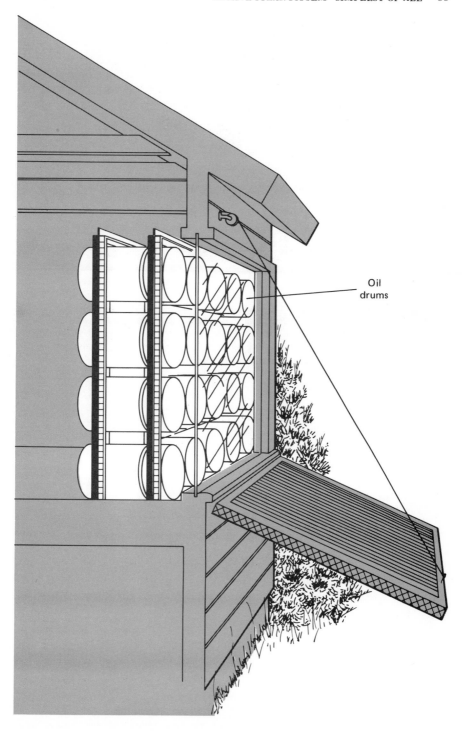

Oil
drums

A greenhouse acts as an effective heat collector for passive systems, and can be a relatively simple addition to most houses. As shown in this drawing from the National Solar Heating and Cooling Information Center, the greenhouse can effectively collect heat from two adjacent sides of the house.

large enough or numerous enough, they introduce a great deal of heat. But they can also *lose* a great deal of heat. For that reason proper insulation and double or triple glazing must be provided for the off periods.

Another popular and common heat-gathering facility is the vertical solar collector. In some versions, this collector merely transmits heat from its black, heat absorbing front out its backside. Other types are constructed so that the heat gathered is emitted by convection air.

When convection is used, the collector is designed so that the heat rises up a "chute" front of the unit, just behind the absorbing surface. From the top the warm air is channeled to deliver heat into the living area at floor level. This starts a flow of convection air that recirculates through the heat collector.

Heat collectors for passive systems may also be located on roofs, just as collectors for active systems are. Again, this passive system moves heated air by natural convection, although it may be necessary in some cases to "hybridize" the system by employing a small fan to force the heated air downward.

INDIRECT-GAIN SYSTEMS. The capacity and efficiency of passive sys-

Tremendous heat gain is possible with an atrium such as the one shown here. Its windowed front and glass roof bring the heat into an area that is surrounded on three sides by the living quarters, into which the heat spreads. Note the berming of earth to window height, an excellent insulating feature.

tems are greater with indirect designs than with direct. Indirect installations involve a heat-storage element specifically designed and positioned to pick up the heat from the collector. This element is usually a massive wall, located directly behind the collector. In some cases, this heat-absorbing mass simply transmits the heat to living quarters by radiation. In others, the engineering provides a flow of air around the mass and throughout the room.

The material used for the storage mass is often masonry of one kind or another. Solar heating engineers select the material, based on its heat-conducting ability, as part of the overall heating plan.

Tanks of water may also be used to provide the storage mass. These tanks may function the same as a masonry mass, or they may be located apart from the collector, fed with heated air by a fan. Here water may be used as a heat storage medium in the same manner as for the bin of boulders described in Chapter 2. The bin for water tanks is constructed much the same way, but water-filled plastic bottles are used instead of boulders.

Pond water on the roof can also be used for heat storage. The water acts both as a collector and a storage unit, radiating its warmth down through the ceiling. The roof pond solar collector also has cooling advantages. In warm weather, its temperature drops during the night. The next day, its cool mass draws heat from the house. Of course, these ponds normally have hinged, insulated covers for sunless periods. And they are used mainly in warmer climates.

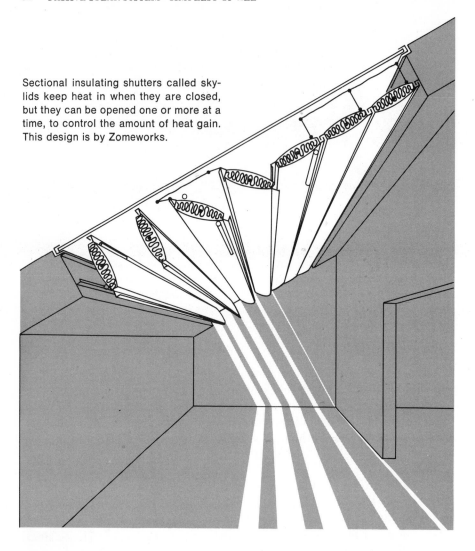

Sectional insulating shutters called sky-lids keep heat in when they are closed, but they can be opened one or more at a time, to control the amount of heat gain. This design is by Zomeworks.

ISOLATED-GAIN SYSTEMS. The isolated-gain system is, basically, a collector that is also a storage unit, located outside the living quarters. It is usually attached to the house, and it radiates heat into occupied areas. The amount of heat admitted is controlled by movable and adjustable insulation.

In some cases, isolated gain systems are not attached to the house but transmit their heat to living quarters by convection. Both are possible because of the natural movement of heated air upward, cold air downward.

HELP FROM THE GREENHOUSE. One of the most attractive and satisfying methods of gaining solar heat the passive way is through a greenhouse

The "Beadwall" insulation system developed by Steve Baer of Zomeworks involves two glass or fiberglass panels separated by two or three inches, the space filled with Styrofoam beads. The beads can be removed by vacuum power when they are not needed and then blown into place when heat must be controlled.

Architect David Wright designed this adobe house in Santa Fe, N.M., specifically for passive solar heating. The double-glazed two-story side of the house faces south. Heat from the sun comes through the windows and heats the massive interior adobe walls—plus water-filled barrels concealed beneath window seats. Solar collectors in front provide domestic hot water via the thermosyphon principle.

Inside the house, an occupant activates plastic-foam shutters which are dropped at night, to hold the heat in. The shutters are manually operated in this house, but could be motorized and activated by heat sensitive controls for fully automatic operation.

The back of this house, which is called Sunscoop, has very few small windows, to reduce heat loss and add to the massive heat collection capabilities of the adobe wall. Further heat control comes from the rise of earth around the house; the floor level is actually three feet below grade. Even the entry, at the left, is solar-energy influenced, designed with two doors, one of which is always closed.

attached to the dwelling. A greenhouse collects a tremendous amount of heat, and this heat can be transmitted into the living quarters through windows and the door. Heat control is possible by adjusting the amount the door and windows are opened.

A typical small greenhouse will build up a temperature of 90 degrees or more, even in winter weather, if it is oriented south, a little west of south, or even west. This is, of course, equivalent to a warm summer day on the outside wall of the house covered by the greenhouse. The result is tremendous support for the regular heating system.

The *atrium* is another combination of growing area and heat collector. It is usually a centrally located "shaft" from the ground up through the roof area, surrounded on all sides by living quarters. Since its purpose is to provide an area for growing plants that are nice to look at, the atrium is surrounded by windows through which the heat is transmitted into the living area.

Heat gain from both the greenhouse and the atrium must be controlled by insulation. In some instances, this control is as simple as plastic-foam insulation batts over the glass where the sunlight enters.

Several of the solar heating features covered in the following chapters are illustrated in this drawing of an Alternative Energies residence in Oklahoma City. The greenhouse, the solar collector, the berming, and the overhang above windows are all part of an efficient solar-energy system.

SPECIAL INSULATING TECHNIQUES. It is important to control the amount of incoming heat as well as the amount of heat loss. So on-and-off insulating techniques have received attention from solar-heat designers. Two systems are outstanding.

One of them is a unit designed much like Venetian blinds, except that the slats are several inches wide and made of insulating material. When the blind is opened, heat or cold can move through the glass surface of windows or collectors. When the blind is closed, the insulating slats form a complete thermal barrier.

Another form of on-and-off insulation is called Beadwall, and is achieved through the insulating value of Styrofoam beads. The Beadwall system requires two layers of glass or plastic on the weather side of the collector. When insulation is necessary, the space between these layers is filled with tiny Styrofoam beads. Thus, the transmission of heat and cold is greatly reduced—almost eliminated. When insulation is not required, the beads are removed. All of this is handled by vacuum-cleaner motors which blow the beads into place or suck them into storage, just as though they were liquid.

In many installations of solar heat systems, the insulation may be no more complicated than heavy draperies that can be drawn over the collection surface.

It is through these insulating control methods that passive systems can keep heat gain and loss within acceptable ranges. As yet there are no delivery systems that can be controlled completely automatically.

5 | Active Liquid Systems

THE PASSIVE solar heating systems discussed in the preceding chapter use natural forces to put the sun to work. Active systems use pumps or blowers to move solar heat from the point of collection to heat domestic water, or to heat a storage tank, or to heat living space, or to heat a swimming pool. The heat may even be pumped through equipment similar to that in a gas-burning refrigerator, to produce cold, instead of heat.

The most common and most efficient medium of heat transmission is a liquid of one kind or another. The liquid can be piped anywhere, at any speed, in any quantity. As it comes from the solar collector, it can be routed through two or more service systems, supplying the energy for different requirements, all from the same collector.

Since the delivery medium for water takes up very little space, it can be set up easily and economically in existing homes. This is especially true with today's plastic piping and tubing materials that are capable of handling heated liquids in situations which may have called for heavy metal piping a few years ago. This is of special significance in retrofit situations, when water-carrying tubing can be run through existing walls. Also, plastic piping is important in do-it-yourself installations, because it is easy to work with. If your plans lean toward metal tubing, soldering of copper presents no problems that are beyond the capabilities of the do-it-yourselfer. Let's start at the beginning.

COLLECTOR FOR LIQUID SYSTEMS. The most common solar heat collector for use with liquid systems is a flat sheet of metal to which metal tubes are welded, soldered, or mechanically fastened. The sheet and the tubes are painted flat black. When the rays of the sun strike the unit, the metal absorbs the heat, which is transferred to the liquid.

Copper and aluminum are favored by many solar heating experts, both because of their excellent heat conductance and their resistance to corro-sion. However, galvanized steel is used extensively, the surfaces exposed to

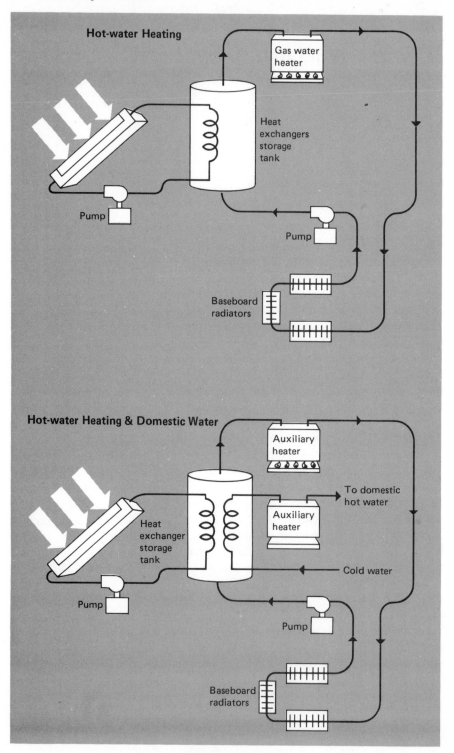

Hot-water Heating

Gas water heater

Heat exchangers storage tank

Pump

Pump

Baseboard radiators

Hot-water Heating & Domestic Water

Auxiliary heater

To domestic hot water

Heat exchanger storage tank

Auxiliary heater

Cold water

Pump

Pump

Baseboard radiators

The two drawings on the previous page show how solar heat can be used for home heating or home heating and domestic water. In both cases, a pump circulates the collector liquid. A heat exchanger picks up the heat for storage. A pump drives the heated water through a hydronic heating system, such as baseboard radiators, picking up added heat from an auxiliary heater if needed. When the solar collector is used for both domestic hot water and for heating, another heat exchanger picks up heat from the storage tank as domestic water circulates. If needed, a second auxiliary heater is used for hot water.

When a liquid system is used to feed a warm-air heating system, the linkage is as shown below. Heated liquid from the collector goes into storage via the heat exchanger. From storage, the heat is picked up by an exchanger and run to a coil in the air-heating chamber. There a fan moves the air past the heated coil and sends warmed air into the heating system. Meanwhile, domestic water is heated by an exchanger in the storage tank. Auxiliary heat is supplied as needed.

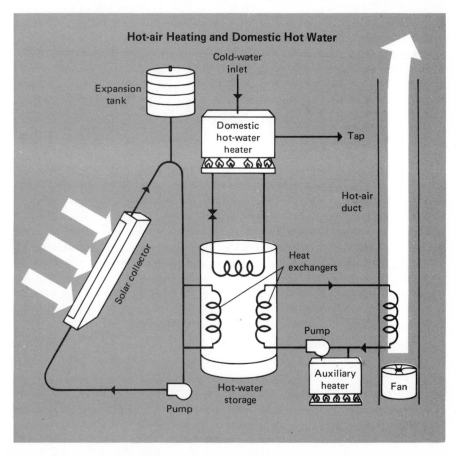

the liquid specially treated to prevent corrosion. In addition, noncorrosive liquids are used in some systems.

Plastic is also used in some low-temperature collectors, usually with plastic or rubber water-carrying tubes.

Then, when liquid is pumped slowly through the collector, it becomes hot. At the other end of the system, the water can be piped into service or into storage for later use.

There are several variations on the flat-plate solar heat collector, most of them engineered to intensify the heating effect of the sun. This is done by prisms, lenses, reflectors, and other methods of controlling the amount of light that strikes the collecting surface. Generally, such devices are intended to reduce the required size of the collector through more efficient absorption of the sun's heat.

One of the most recent and efficient modifications of the collector involves a vacuum-tube design. The collector is composed of double-walled glass tube, with a vacuum between the two walls. The inner tube is blackened so that it will absorb the heat of the sun. The heat, however, cannot escape back into the atmosphere because of the vacuum-bottle effect. Inside the inner glass tube is a metal heat-absorber which is fitted with metal tubes through which the liquid circulates. These tubes are teamed up, as many as are necessary, in collector units.

Generally, the more sophisticated collectors are most effective when the available room for a collector is small. When the situation permits a collector of larger size, however, the flat-sheet collector produces so much heat that it must be controlled with automatic off-on switches.

In addition to the actual heat-absorbing surface and the tubing which carries the liquid, collectors have two essential components. One of them is insulation behind the heat-collecting plate. This prevents the loss of heat from the back of the unit. Insulation is also frequently provided around the perimeter of the absorber plate, to reduce heat loss. (Sometimes you'll see a molding six-inches wide, or so, around the perimeter of an entire collector array, covering added insulation.)

Insulation presents somewhat of a problem in solar collectors, in view of the fact that the temperature inside the collector box may reach 300°F or more. This would melt the popular—and highly efficient—rigid plastic foam insulation material. It does not, however, affect glass-wool insulation. Therefore, the glass material may be used by itself. Sometimes glass wool is used *between the collector and a thickness of foam,* thus protecting the foam from melting while at the same time taking advantage of the extra insulating value of foam.

The other essential component in the collector is the glass cover, which prevents the loss of heat to the atmosphere. (Not all collectors have glazing. Some, notably those for low-temperature applications, such as swimming pool heating, are unglazed.) Collectors are usually either single- or double-

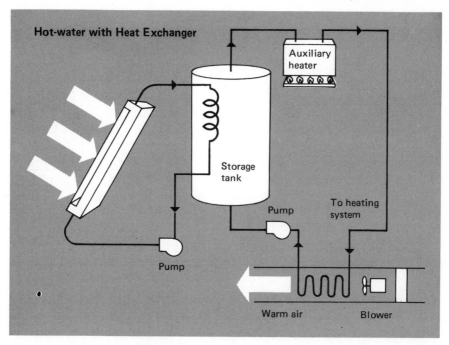

Hot-water with Heat Exchanger

Auxiliary heater

Storage tank

Pump

To heating system

Pump

Warm air

Blower

When there is danger of freezing, a system such as this permits the use of anti-freeze liquid. This liquid is pumped through the collector and into a heat exchanger in the storage tank. There it heats the water, which circulates through the residential heating system (which may be hydronic) or through another heat exchanger to transfer the liquid to an air system. The same setup can include domestic water heating through a line which includes an auxiliary heater.

glazed. The choice depends on how high a temperature is desired in the collectors and in what climatic area they will be used. For heating domestic water in Florida, for example, single-glazed collectors would perform acceptably. On the other hand, for space heating in Minnesota, a double-glazed collector would likely do better.

In some collectors, heat distribution is achieved through prismatic segmentation of the glass. The glass need not be transparently clear. There are types of glass which permit the entrance of solar heat, but obstruct the view from the outside. This is an important factor in collectors used in window situations, but in some cases it also helps hold the heat within the collector.

Another type of glass is "stippled" in a way that allows maximum entry of heat even when the sun is at a relatively flat angle—as it is in the morning and the afternoon. This type of glass makes it possible to use collectors that are not ideally oriented. As well, because the liquid is pumped through the collector, with no dependence on natural convection, the collector can be

Liquid Collectors

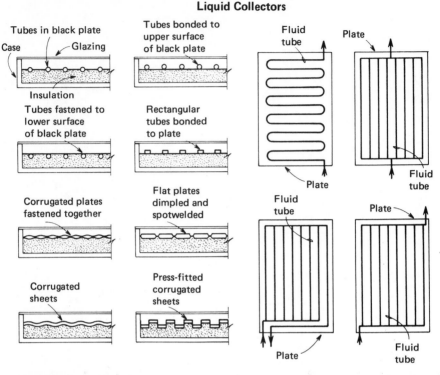

Eight different forms of flat collectors are shown here, along with four different routes the heat-absorbing liquid can take. All of these forms are available commercially, and some of them are simple enough for home construction in a do-it-yourself system.

set at any angle. There are special collector mounts that allow adjustments of angle. This makes it possible to adjust the angle of collector so that it takes the best advantage of the sun's angle at all times of the year. The collector may be lowered to a flatter angle in the summer and raised to a higher angle in the winter—unless, of course, the collector is mounted in a single rigid position on a roof.

Still another method of increasing collection efficiency is through the use of an "arched" acrylic plastic cover which functions much like a Fresnel lens. The curved lens surface concentrates the sun's rays on a heat-collector tube which is painted black and slightly flattened to provide better receiving power. Because of the arched shape of the plastic cover, the collector picks up early-morning sunlight on one side of the arch, works at top efficiency throughout the day, and picks up late-hour sun through the other side of the arch.

Despite the notable advantages of liquid heat distribution systems, there are disadvantages. One of them is the danger of leaks. Chances of leaks are

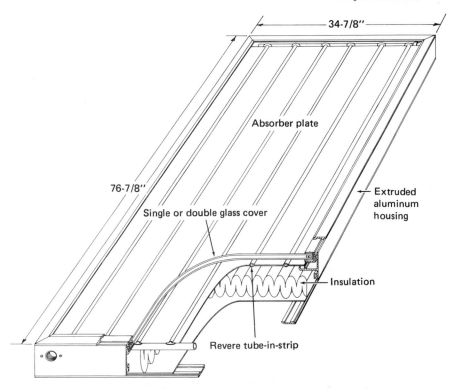

34-7/8"

Absorber plate

76-7/8"

Extruded
aluminum
housing

Single or double glass cover

Insulation

Revere tube-in-strip

Basic components of a solar collector are shown in this drawing of a Revere Sunaid. The liquid enters the collector at lower left and runs to the top through tubes bonded to the absorber plate. Heated, the water exits at upper left. Insulation prevents heat loss through the back. Double glazing prevents heat loss through the front. Gentle pumping keeps the liquid in circulation.

small in well-assembled systems, with metal tubing carefully soldered or plastic tubing carefully "chemical-welded." Although corrosion might eventually attack any metal carrying water, there are special liquids and chemicals that eliminate this possibility. As a means of helping you determine the actual source of a leak, some of the liquids used in solar collectors may be colored to make them easily recognizable. This feature is feasible only in systems which circulate the heated water through the heat-storage complex, and do not heat drinking water directly in the collectors.

Freezing is another danger, but it can be avoided either by automatic draining of the outdoor sections of the system at night, or by the use of antifreeze in the water, or by employing liquids that cannot freeze.

When one of the antifreeze liquids is used, the liquid cannot be allowed to mix with water in the storage tank. That is why a heat exchanger is installed in the storage tank. The exchanger may be simply a long coil of

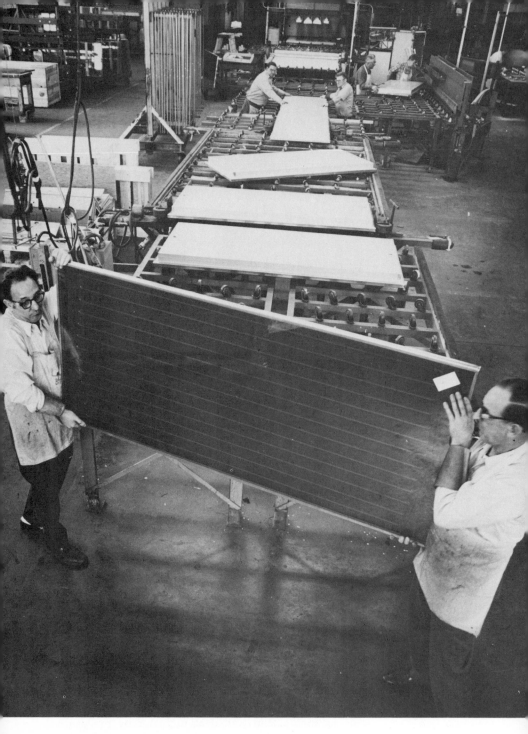

Collectors come from the factory complete and ready for installation in as many units as may be needed for the heat requirements. The unit shown is by PPG Industries. Typically, these units can be mounted on the roof if the pitch is appropriate, or on mounts that can be adjusted to seasonal changes in solar angle.

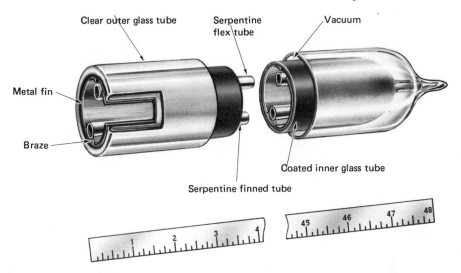

This collector tube developed by GE employs principles of the simple vacuum bottle. There are two tubes interspaced by a vacuum. The inner tube, painted black, collects the heat. The vacuum locks the heat in. Inside the tube is a metal fin which picks up the heat and releases it to a liquid running through tubes which spiral through the collector.

tubing, that puts as much heated pipe as possible into contact with the water in the storage tank.

LIQUID HEAT STORAGE. The standard storage unit for liquid solar heat systems is a big tank of water. Brand new septic tanks are often used for this purpose. However, if you are using such a tank above ground, it must be supported on all sides with earth or otherwise reinforced so the liquid doesn't burst the tank. Thick insulation, completely encompassing the tank, is essential. Of course, the best location for the storage tank is *inside* the home's heated space. That way, whatever heat does escape from the tank contributes heat to the home.

When the system produces heat for domestic water only, the simplest arrangement is one that circulates the water continuously through the collector and the tank. An outlet leads to the plumbing system to deliver the heated water. An inlet keeps the storage tank filled with new water as the heated water is drawn off. As mentioned above, it may be necessary to provide automatic drainage of the collector to prevent freezing in winter weather. You can use a thermostatically controlled on-off switch to keep the water from reaching too high a temperature. An alternative is to use a tempering valve. This device mixes cold water with hot water as it exits the storage tank to reduce tap water to a temperature that won't burn you. Typical settings range from 120 to 140°F. That way you can let the sun

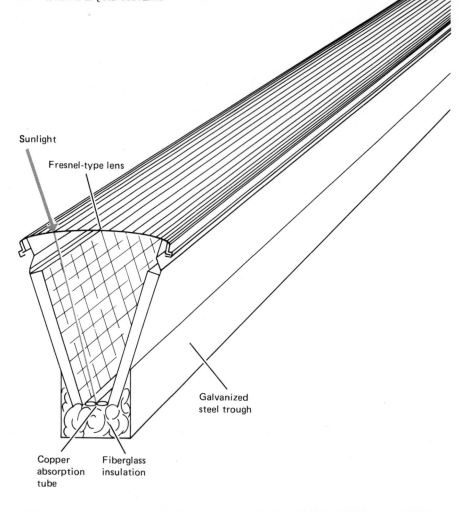

Sunlight

Fresnel-type lens

Galvanized
steel trough

Copper
absorption
tube

Fiberglass
insulation

This collector unit by Northrup, Inc., utilizes an arched Fresnel-type lens which picks up sunlight from morning to night and directs it to the collector at the bottom of the insulated V. The units are mounted in a frame and can be rotated by an electric motor to track the sun, for day-long efficiency.

heat the storage tank to as high a temperature as it can in order to collect maximum amounts of heat. (On hot summer days, water temperatures in the collector may rise as high as 185°F.)

If the solar heat is used to heat the house, the water may be fed through "hydronic" radiators, which are usually the baseboard type. The water temperature recommended for these radiators is about 160°F. Since the water temperatures from a solar heating system may not be this high, designers increase the amount of hot water in the radiators, for added radiation of heat. This can be done by increasing the lengths of the radiators or by increasing the diameter of the tube-and-fin heat exchangers in the radiators.

Liquid-type solar heat systems can also be used for heating a home with air. A water-to-air heat exchanger (usually a long finned tube) releases the heat to air in a blower chamber. Then the air is circulated via ducts to the warm-air registers and back to the heat exchanger for reheating.

BASIC BUYING SUGGESTIONS. When you shop for components which you yourself will assemble into a solar heating system, or when you discuss solar heating with a commercial outfit, use more than just price as your determinants. Also consider the following:

• Square footage is not by itself a determining factor. Higher efficiency may do the job with smaller area. Important factors affecting efficiency include absorption ability, the number of glass layers, the degree of insulation, and the energy required to keep the liquid in motion.

• Installation requirements can vary from do-it-yourself simple ones to high-cost and complex commercial ones. Compare component costs *plus* installation costs. In some cases, the simpler, less expensive unit may require expensive installation.

• Look for ease of repair and maintenance. For example, a collector with an easily removable glass cover for access to the collector plate and tubing may be more desirable than a collector which must be completely dismantled.

• Investigate the demands such as orientation, pitch, and so on, to find which of the available systems are best suited to your climate. This suggests, of course, that you may be better off dealing with a local solar-heating concern than one that may be more famous but not as familiar with requirements for your locality.

• Most important of all, look into the life-expectancy of *all* the materials in the system. Note the emphasis on *all:* In Australia, where solar heating has been employed for more than 20 years, a frequent source of failure of solar collectors has been the sheet metal pan protecting the collector insulation on the back. The absorber plate and glass covers have worked just fine, but the pan has been known to rust out, requiring replacement.

6 | Active Air Systems

IF YOUR HOUSE already has warm-air heating, your thinking should lean toward a solar *active-air* system. The same may be true if you are planning a new house. Solar-heated active-air systems are simple to link into standard warm-air heating, because they function in much the same way. The system collects heat from the sun by means of a specially designed collector—then transmits it throughout the house in essentially the same way as fuel-fired warm-air systems do, through ducts and blowers.

Active-air systems, however, are not restricted to basic house heating. Through the use of heat exchangers, they can be used to heat domestic water—and they can be designed to heat a *liquid sub-system,* such as a swimming pool or an out-building or an addition to which the transfer of heat would be simple with liquid and impractical with air.

AIR COLLECTOR SYSTEMS. From the outside, a solar energy collector engineered for an air system may look little different from one intended for a liquid system. The frame, the glass cover, the collector "plate," and the insulation are all there. The difference lies in the "flow channels." Air collectors take advantage of the "fin" principle—which, as a matter of interest, is the principle involved in controlling heat in your automobile. The fins are a number of thin metal components, attached to a tube or duct, which increase greatly the effective exposure of metal surface to air—or to liquid. This increased exposure increases the transfer of heat from one element to the other. *The more surface, the greater the transfer.*

In its simplest and most effective form, the collector is a sheet of metal—painted black on the top, so that it will absorb the sun's heat. On the back, there are many fins, which carry the solar heat through the sheet into a chamber through which air moves. As it passes through this chamber, the air picks up heat from the fins. At the top of the chamber, the air is operationally hot, ready for transport into storage.

Since convection is a strong factor in warm air, and since most of the passages through which warmed air travels are relatively large, passive air systems are common, as covered in preceding chapters. However, the greatest efficiency of warm-air systems depends on physical movement of the air—mainly because it is very often necessary to drive the warmed air downward, against the flow of natural convection. Of course, it is unwise to fight those laws too vigorously, so the most effective and economical warm-air solar energy systems try to take advantage of convection plus fans and gentle blowers.

AIR-SYSTEM COLLECTORS. Solar collectors that produce hot air differ very little in overall principle from those that heat a liquid. There is a collector plate inside a frame, backed up by insulation, and covered with glass or other translucent material. Instead of tubing, the collectors have relatively large ducts or flues, through which air moves. There are, also, air collector units employing the same V principle often used for fluid collectors, as described in the preceding chapter. These concentrate the sun's heat on a passageway filled with moving air.

The heat-absorbing surface may be blackened copper, aluminum, or galvanized metal. Or it may be a sheet that is double-coated—once with a heat-confining surface that transmits the heat through the metal, once with a heat-absorbing surface that picks up the solar energy.

In its simplest form, the collector may consist of just a sandwich composed of the heat-absorbing metal, a few inches of air space, and a backing of insulation. The air moves through the air space, picking up heat.

As with all collectors, there is a glazed covering that holds the heat in. In many cases the glazing may be double, for extra insulation. Since the typical unit picks up heat only during the ideal sunlight hours, efficient storage is essential for periods when the sun isn't shining.

Some of the manufacturers of air-heating systems recommend the use of

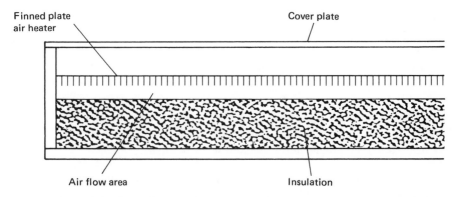

Finned plate air heater

Cover plate

Air flow area

Insulation

This cross-sectional drawing shows the elements of the air collector. The collector plate is finned to provide maximum possible air-to-metal contact. The cover plate can be glass or a plastic material. Double glazing helps retain heat.

roof-top collectors. Others produce collectors which stand vertically, and have the appearance of windows. When vertical collectors are used, it is possible to fasten the back of the "sandwich" to the sheathing of the building. This results in heat gain through the wall, in addition to the heating that comes from blowing warmed air through ducts into areas not exposed to the radiation from the back of the collector. The vertical collector is better adapted to new construction than to retrofit situations.

MOVING THE AIR WHERE IT IS NEEDED. The route heated air takes through a residence is shown in the accompanying drawing. Here are details:

A. The air picks up heat from the collector, which would be much larger than indicated in the drawing.

B. A fan or blower keeps the air in motion, feeding it into the collector. Only one small fan is required for normal residential heating.

C. Heated, the air is blown through ducts directly into the storage tank.

D. The storage tank for warm-air systems is a bin filled with small rocks, as described in Chapter 2. The heated air, passing through the bin, heats the rocks, as well as the concrete walls of the bin. Although the air loses some of its heat, transferring it to the rocks, it still remains hot enough to keep the house warm as it moves on through the system.

E. Air returns to the collector for re-heating, then back again to the storage bin, to keep it heated.

F. Heated air is blown into the heating system of the house. In this drawing, it is shown going through the furnace into the delivery system.

G. The warm-air furnace is included in the drawing to illustrate the way it can come into use as a backup when the demand is too great for solar heat alone. When the heat from the sun is adequate, the furnace stands by. If the demand should rise above the capabilities of solar heat, the furnace comes on and adds its heat to the circulating air.

H. Ducts deliver the warmed air to all parts of the house.

I. Warmed air enters the rooms of the house through warm-air registers. The amount of heat admitted to each room may be controlled by opening or closing the registers, or by dampers along the duct lines.

J. Forced by the gentle circulation fan, the air that comes into the room is returned to the storage bin for reheating.

As this brief description of the air-heating system shows, the delivery of solar-heated air throughout the home is no more complicated than when heat from a fuel burner is used. Since so many homes already employ warm-air heat, active-air solar-energy is gaining in popularity.

HOT-AIR STORAGE BINS. Although there are several different types of hot-air storage units, the principle is the same for all. Air passes through a chamber filled with heat-absorbing materials. When the air is hot, it leaves

Typical Air, Solar-heating System

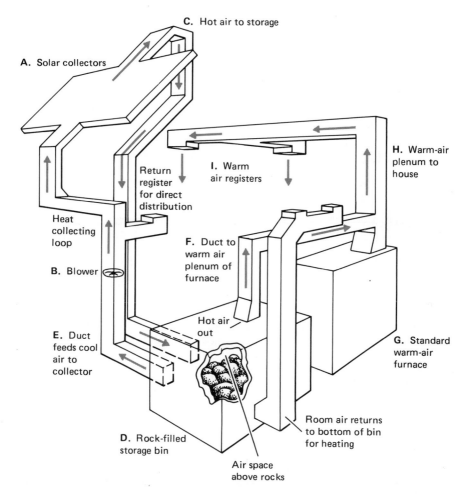

C. Hot air to storage

A. Solar collectors

H. Warm-air plenum to house

Return register for direct distribution

I. Warm air registers

Heat collecting loop

B. Blower

F. Duct to warm air plenum of furnace

E. Duct feeds cool air to collector

Hot air out

G. Standard warm-air furnace

D. Rock-filled storage bin

Room air returns to bottom of bin for heating

Air space above rocks

This drawing illustrates the basic principles of warm-air heating as described in the accompanying text.

some of its heat with these absorbing masses. When the air is cool, it picks up warmth that has been previously transferred to storage.

The most common material for storage walls is concrete or concrete block. Commercial suppliers of solar heat equipment specify either concrete or boxes of plywood built on 2×4 or 2×6 studs. In either case, insulation is necessary to prevent the heat from escaping. An insulation value of at least R-11 is recommended in most cases.

It is a relatively simple job for the do-it-yourselfer to build a storage unit,

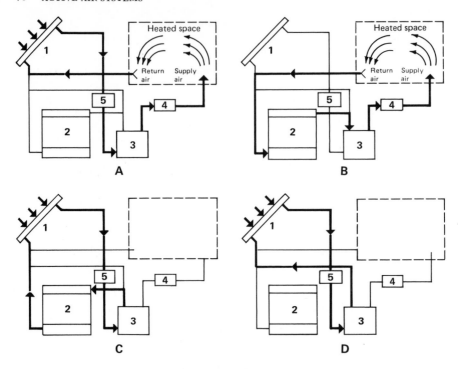

1. Collector **2.** Storage **3.** Air-handling unit
4. Auxiliary heater **5.** Domestic-water pre heater

These drawings show the complete operational versatility of a warm-air system produced by Solaron. In drawing A, the heat is coming from the collector only. In B the storage bin provides the heat during a period when the sun is not shining. In C, the house is warm enough, so the collector is storing heat. In D the air handling unit, with motorized dampers, has shut down the warming circuits and the heat is drawn from domestic water heating only.

filling it with the boulders or pebbles that are standard throughout the industry. Some authorities recommend baseball-size boulders, while others lean toward pebbles averaging an inch in diameter. The pebbles tend to "stratify" the heat, maintaining higher temperature near the top of the storage unit, cooler near the bottom.

It works like this: Air, heated by collectors to, say, 140°F, enters the rock storage bin at the top. It is forced down through the rock, transferring

An air-heating system (shown right) can be used for cooling, with the storage bin acting as a cold-storage unit. At night a fan drives cool night air through the storage bin, cooling its contents. The hot air in the chamber is driven outside. The next day, the system moves air through the storage bin, where it is cooled before it flows into the living area.

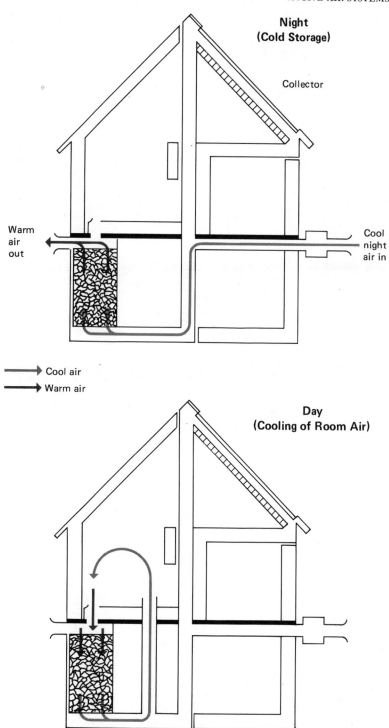

**Night
(Cold Storage)**

Collector

Warm
air
out

Cool
night
air in

Cool air

Warm air

**Day
(Cooling of Room Air)**

Tremendous quantities of heat can be stored in rock bins the size of this one, of concrete poured in a basement before the house itself was built. Openings for the ducts that will carry air in and out of the bin are at the bottom and top of the near side. Size of the rocks used is indicated by those on the floor at the left of the bin. Hot-air storage bins are also made of concrete block or wood.

its heat until at the bottom it exits at, say 70°F. It is returned to the collectors for reheating at this temperature, which assures that the collectors will run at high efficiency. Over the course of a sunny day's collection, the rock in the storage bin is gradually heated, with the hottest rock on top and the coldest at the bottom, and with the stratification level gradually moving downward. At night or during cloudy weather when you wish to heat from storage, air is blown in at the bottom and removed from the top. In this way air at the highest temperature in storage is removed for use in space heating.

Some manufacturers of solar heating equipment also utilize the "cold storage" facilities of pebbles. During the summer, cool night-time air is blown through the storage bin, cooling the pebbles. The next day, when cooling is needed in the house, the system circulates warm room air through the collector, causing it to lose heat to the cool pebbles.

Still another type of storage unit takes advantage of the chemical-physical reaction to heat of a material called "eutectic salt"—actually sodium sulphate decahydrate. It is used in storage units sold by Solar, Inc., and introduced under the name "Solar-Aire."

Eutectic salts store a tremendous quantity of heat in relatively little space. At a relatively low heat level—around 90°F—the salts change to a liquid, which is their heat-storing form. Since the change occurs at such a low temperature, storage is accomplished even on partially cloudy days, when solar heat doesn't reach normally high levels. The storage life of the salts is relatively long, and delivery of warmed air is the same as for other storage masses.

DOMESTIC HOT WATER FROM AIR. For active-air collectors a heat exchanger can be used to transfer some of the heat to the domestic water supply. Usually a conventional hot water heater is needed to carry part of the load.

Most heat exchangers are coiled tubes. Water moves through the tube, while hot air circulates around it, transmitting heat to the water through the walls of the coiled tube. In another form, the hot air passes through a finned chamber which is submerged in the water. The fins provide a relatively large area of metal-to-water contact for the transfer of heat. Regardless of the specific design of the system, the important factor is the amount of metal-to-water area. The larger this area is, the more heat is transferred from the air to the water.

Solar heating can greatly reduce fuel costs for domestic hot water. The solar heat warms the cold water (it may be as low as 40°F) before the water goes into the standard heater, cutting down greatly the amount of fuel or electricity needed to boost the temperature for domestic needs (120-140°F). The only mechanical aid required is a small pump to circulate the water through the heat exchanger and the preheating tank and a small blower to circulate the air from collectors to the heat exchanger. Solaron makes such a system.

7 | Heating Water for Kitchen, Bath, and Laundry

SOLAR-HEATED domestic water involves the simplest and least expensive of all solar heat installations. Several systems are available commercially for as little as $1,000, installed and ready to start saving you money on other energy sources. Before long, the unit pays for itself. The savings have been demonstrated throughout the world. In parts of Australia, solar water heaters are required by law. In Japan, the heaters have been selling at a rate of around 150,000 units a year. In the U.S. the number of solar domestic water heaters is increasing steadily.

Solar-heated domestic water is economical mainly because only a relatively small collector is needed. While residential heating may require a collector area one-third to one-half of the floor area of the house, the collector for hot water may be a 4×8-foot unit. If demands on hot water are particularly high, or if the amount of annual sunlight is low, two units may be needed. With a collector area as small as this, you may be able to obtain as much as 90 percent of your household needs, figuring 50 gallons a day for a family of four.

There are, also, special collectors designed for water heating. These units employ larger tubing to circulate a greater amount of water than goes through collectors designed for home heating, and thus they can serve for some of the hot-water storage needs.

Installation of a system involves no more than the simplest plumbing techniques, making it an easy do-it-yourself project. The standard procedure is to link the solar-heated water circuit with an electric heater or a fuel burner, so that the sun reduces the need for auxiliary heat. The savings are greatest for electric heaters but they are also significant when fuel burners are used.

The first consideration when you start planning for solar-heated domestic water is the amount of hot water your family needs. A family of four will generally use 50 gallons of hot water a day. If there are unusually high amounts of showering, laundering, or dishwashing, the demand may be greater. A fairly accurate estimate of your needs is important, since it determines the capacity of the solar collector system you will need.

Since you will need only a relatively small, easy-to-install collector, you may want to consider an adjustable mount. These mounts let you adjust the angle of the collector to take best advantage of the sun, month by month. As the table below from Grumman Aerospace shows, there is considerable difference in collector temperatures, month to month, and from one angle to another.

The table is figured for a latitude of 40 degrees. The common practice is to add 10 degrees to the latitude you live in to determine the proper angle from horizontal. Thus, a 50-degree angle is proper for the 40-degree latitude. As the table shows, the performance decreases as the angle varies from the ideal 50 degrees during winter months. In the summer, however, when the sun is higher, the flatter angle performs best. (If you don't know the latitude where you live, consult the map in Chapter 9.)

MONTH	TEMPERATURE IN COLLECTOR AT END OF DAY		
	50-DEGREE *Angle*	40-DEGREE *Angle*	30-DEGREE *Angle*
January	131°F	126°F	118°F
February	140	136	130
March	146	147	145
April	145	150	153
May	144	152	157
June	143	153	160
July	147	156	162
August	151	157	161
September	154	157	157
October	150	149	145
November	139	135	128
December	128	123	115

This table is based on a system that takes in water at 50°F and heats it in a 50-gallon tank to a temperature of 160°F. The figures are based on average weather conditions.

If you live in a latitude south of 40 degrees, you can adapt the table to your situation by using the latitude-plus-10 formula. This will modify the degree angle at the top of the table, but will produce essentially parallel temperatures in the columns, month by month.

BACKUP REQUIREMENTS. Solar heat probably won't be able to maintain your domestic water at required temperatures throughout the day or throughout the year. Daytime cloudiness, nighttime darkness, and domestic

Domestic solar water heaters often come in kits, ready for installation by the homeowner. This one is from Alten Corporation.

consumption of hot water are the chief variables. The storage tank compensates for these variables by building up a supply of heated water. But the tank needs backup during long winter nights, and during long cloudy spells in all seasons. The support can come from electric or fuel-burning systems that turn on as needed. Simple on-off controls, activated by heat, turn the backup on when the water temperature drops below a preset level and off when solar energy raises the water temperature sufficiently.

The standard support system works this way:

• Cold water from the water main enters the storage tank as needed to replace water tapped for domestic use.

• The solar-collector system heats the water to the required temperature —and maintains that temperature as best it can.

• From the storage tank, water is routed to the regular water-heating equipment. As long as the water is hot enough, it merely travels through the tank and into domestic use.

• If the water from the solar-heated tank enters the tank of the backup heater at a temperature below that required, the heater automatically comes on. Relatively little fuel is used, since the heater receives water that is at least partly heated at all times.

• When the demand tapers off or the solar heat increases, water in the solar storage tank becomes hotter. At the required temperature, the backup system will automatically shut off, returning the entire heating job to the solar-heated part of the system.

AN EASY-TO-MAKE COLLECTOR. A collector that is easily within the capability of the average do-it-yourselfer can be put together, using solder and copper tubing. The unit measures 4×8 feet and produces many gallons of water at appropriate temperatures. (The dimensions cannot be given exactly, since they depend on exact working conditions, but you can adapt them as you go along.) In northern climates, you may need two units, but it is a good idea to put one together, give it a try, and build the second one only if the single unit doesn't do the job. Linking the two together involves simple plumbing. (Instructions are covered in greater detail in Chapter 10.)

Start by making the "box" that the collection elements are housed in. Use a sheet of exterior-grade plywood ½-inch thick if the collector will rest on a supporting surface—¾-inch thick if it will be supported only at corners or edges. Cut redwood or cedar preservative-treated 2×4s to make a 4×8 frame to which the plywood can be nailed.

The next step is to make a "grid" of ¾-inch copper tubing that will fit inside the box with about two inches of space all around. The grid is assembled with elbows and Ts, as shown in the accompanying drawing. The exact length of the tubing components will depend on the way they fit into the couplings and the way the entire unit fits into the box. *Be sure to buy lightweight tubing and elbows and Ts that are intended for soldering.*

Working on a flat surface, fit the components together. Use steelwool on all mating surfaces, to ensure watertight soldered joints. Also, take pains to ream the inside of all ends after they have been cut, to minimize friction when the collector is in use.

The grid of tubing must be fastened to a heat-absorbing base. One way to do this is to cut strips of copper flashing to the proper length and solder the vertical tubing to them. Another method is to cut a single sheet of galvanized metal to the proper size and solder the tubes to it. Be sure that the tubing has been "steelwooled" gleaming clean and that the surface of the backup material is clean also. Make the solder joint as close to complete as possible, which is easiest with liberal use of solder and flux.

The collector must have insulation in back of the grid. Fiberglass is usually the best insulation, since it is not affected by the excessive heat which the collector will pick up. Put two or more inches in the bottom of the box.

Put the grid in place temporarily to mark the points in the 2×4s where you must bore holes for the inlet and outlet pipes.

Now spray-paint the grid flat black. Put it back in the box and insert short lengths of tubing into the inlet and outlet Ts before soldering them in place.

The final step in construction involves the glass cover. Put together a frame made of storm-window stock, measuring 4×8 feet. It should have a cross member in the middle, to support the glass. Play it safe by using shatterproof glass or a heavy sheet plastic such as Plexiglas. Make sure the puttying job is leakproof, which is easiest to do with one of the plastic caulking materials.

WATER-HEATING SYSTEMS: THERMOSIPHON AND SINGLE TANK

1

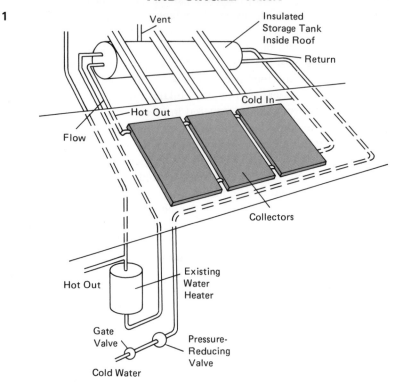

Vent

Insulated
Storage Tank
Inside Roof

Return

Cold In

Hot Out

Flow

Collectors

Existing
Water
Heater

Hot Out

Gate
Valve

Pressure-
Reducing
Valve

Cold Water

2

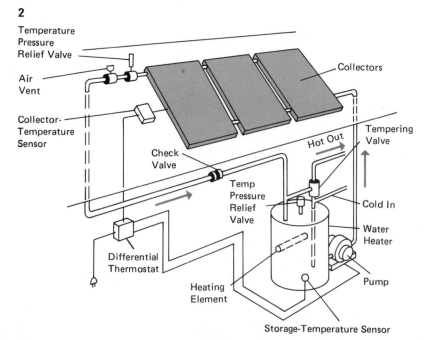

Temperature
Pressure
Relief Valve

Air
Vent

Collectors

Collector-
Temperature
Sensor

Tempering
Valve

Hot Out

Check
Valve

Temp
Pressure
Relief
Valve

Cold In

Water
Heater

Differential
Thermostat

Pump

Heating
Element

Storage-Temperature Sensor

On the preceding page, drawing 1 shows the **thermosiphon,** or natural circulation system, in which cold water falls through collectors, absorbing heat, then rises to the storage tank above. To prevent heat loss by reverse flow at night, the tank must be at least one foot above the collectors. In areas where freezing temperatures occur, a nonfreezing solution can be circulated using the same principle with a heat exchanger in the tank. The system shown is by Sun Power, New Zealand. The thermosiphon system is the simplest, with no energy input. In drawing 2, a **single-tank** pumped system has backup electric heating elements near top of tank. This system, by Energy Systems, Inc., is useful when an older system must be replaced or when a new installation is made. Water from bottom of the tank is pumped through collectors, where it is heated and returned to the top of the tank. Drawings courtesy of *Popular Science* magazine.

Mount the framed glass cover on the collector box with screws so that it can be removed if necessary for maintenance. Caulking around this joint will further ensure resistance to the weather.

From this point on all you need to do is hook the collector into the water system as shown in the accompanying drawings. Note that the drawings are oversimplified in order to make basics clear. They do not show all of the components which may be necessary in your area. Check things out with a local expert to make sure that your system will perform properly and at top efficiency. One thing you should surely check is the possibility of switching to plastic tubing for the hookup, since it is easiest to work with in many situations.

In order to prevent the loss of heat already collected, you should insulate the tubing which carries the water to storage, and also insulate the storage tank. There are special insulating wraps for pipes. You can use ordinary fiberglass batts around the tank. In the interest of efficiency, be sure to insulate all heat-loss possibilities. This will cut down on the amount of time your backup heater will need to operate.

Another feature that saves energy is a check valve which shuts off the circulation of water whenever the temperature in the tank is greater than that in the collector. This prevents the system from working backward.

In the colder parts of the country, you must include a drain system that will empty the collector when the sun goes down and there is danger of freezing. Any well-engineered commercial system will have this feature. If you make your own, buy an automatic drain control, activated by *temperature readings*. This type of control not only drains the collector during freezing nights, but also leaves it empty during sunless days and subfreezing temperatures.

If your collector will be drained to avoid freezing, it should be tilted at least 5 degrees so that the water will run out rapidly and completely. This will be a problem in relatively few cases, since the best-engineered collectors are tilted more steeply than that for best exposure to the sun.

FULL-CIRCULATION AND INDIRECT SOLAR WATER HEATING SYSTEMS

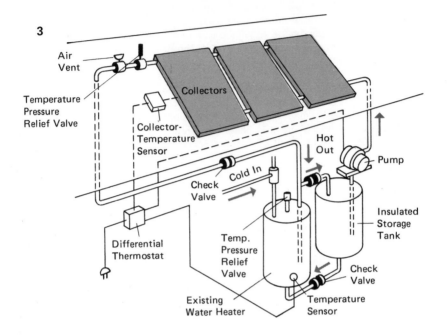

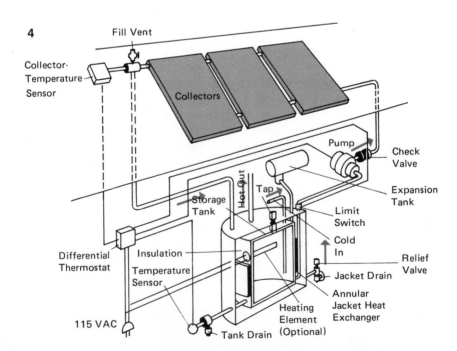

The **full-circulation** system, in drawing 3, is ideal for retrofits, tying in with an existing electric or gas heating system. A loop connects the existing water tank and insulated storage tank so the sun can heat water in both. A tempering valve mixes cold and hot water to lower the temperature to a safe level (typically 120° to 140° F), since sun-heated water can reach temperatures up to 185°. The ESI direct heating type here automatically drains in case of freezing temperatures. The **indirect** (or closed loop) system (drawing 4) heats water in the storage tank by means of a heat exchanger that is either inside the tank or wrapped around it (shown). Nonfreezing heat-transfer fluid need not be drained from collectors. Note that local codes often require double-walled heat exchangers when a toxic antifreeze is used in a potable system. Indirect systems can use one tank (shown) or two. These drawings were adapted courtesy of *Popular Science* magazine.

There are solar heat collectors intended for domestic water heating that use antifreeze, instead of circulating the actual domestic water. These systems feed the heated liquid through a heat exchanger inside the water tank. When this method of heating is used, it is extremely important that the non-potable liquid does not leak into the tank. As a guarantee against this, good commercial units are carefully tested before installation. Testing after the system is installed can sometimes be done by filling the circulation system with soap-sudsy water and applying air pressure to produce bubbles that indicate leaks.

Although domestic water heating is most efficient with liquid systems, hot-air installations may include water heating as part of their function. This is done with heat exchangers. Or, in some cases, a hot water storage tank is embedded in the boulders and pebbles of the hot-air storage bin. There it picks up heat from contact with the stones and from the warm air circulating around it, preheating water for the prime water heater.

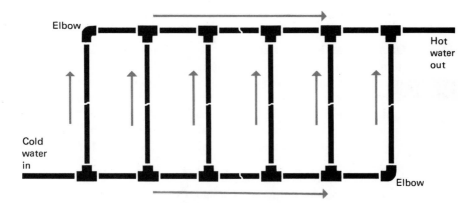

You can assemble a collector system easily, following the pattern of tubes, elbows, and Ts in this drawing. Use copper tubing intended for soldered joints. See the text beginning on page 85 for assembly and installation instructions.

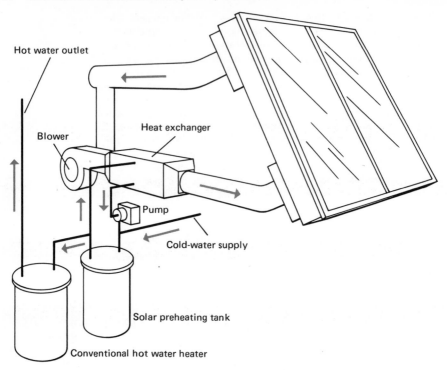

Hot water outlet

Blower

Heat exchanger

Pump

Cold-water supply

Solar preheating tank

Conventional hot water heater

This drawing shows how a solar air collector can be used to preheat water entering a conventional hot-water heater, thereby reducing costs of heating water with standard fuel. Hot air from the collector circulates through the heat exchanger, where it heats water that is circulated by means of a small pump. With much of its heat already provided by the sun, the water moves to the conventional tank where it receives any required additional heat.

THE STORAGE TANK. The size of the storage tank for a domestic hot water system is a strong factor in performance. A small tank will heat quickly, and come to a high temperature on normal sunlit days. It will, however, cool off faster when the hot water is used. This is because of the constant replenishment with cold water as the hot water is drawn off.

On the other hand, a bigger tank will take more sunlight to heat, and may go through long periods when the temperature is below the required level. Yet it will deliver a greater amount of heated water into the system without dropping sharply in temperature.

In your investigation of equipment as related to your climate, if you find collectors relatively inexpensive, you may want to use a larger tank and a large collector for greatest cost-effectiveness over the years.

In a typical situation, a family of four would be able to get along with

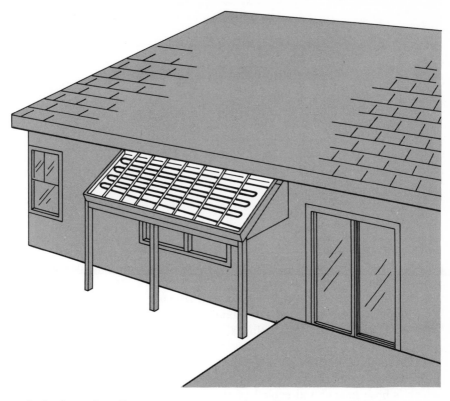

A simple awning allows you to mount a solar collector on top. This makes an attractive addition, and can be put up on whichever side of the house has the best solar exposure. This collector is from the Florida Conservation Center.

a storage tank holding about 75 gallons of water—fed by a collector scaled to keep that amount of water effectively hot and to minimize the need for a backup heater.

For information about solar water heating in your locality and for names of dealers in your area, contact the National Solar Heating and Cooling Information Center, P.O. Box 1607, Rockville, MD 20850.

8 | Cooling with the Sun

THE USE OF SOLAR COOLING for homes has not been as popular as solar cooling for commercial buildings. But undoubtedly, home systems with solar-cooling capabilities will be increasingly common. In the previous chapter, we described a cooling system which took advantage of the cool nighttime air, storing it in a rock-filled bin. Some innovative solar-energy companies have developed methods of using solar heat the way a refrigerator may use gas heat.

One company that has been working extensively on solar cooling is Arkla Industries. Late in 1977, Arkla unveiled a solar energy home in Indiana which is both heated and cooled by the sun. At this point, the high cost of the system limits the market, but the principles will no doubt be streamlined enough to make solar cooling an affordable feature in homes using solar energy for heat.

The house that Arkla has developed into a heat-and-cool model looks like a regular two-and-one-half-story dwelling, with a standard double-pitch roof. On the sunny side of the roof a collector covers more than 800 square feet of space. It is comprised of forty-eight Arkla Solaire collectors, and provides about 75 percent of the heating and cooling requirements.

The house contains more than 3200 square feet of living space. There are four bedrooms, three and a half baths, and a full basement for both storage and recreation. Arkla built the house in cooperation with the U.S. government. Arkla points out that the Department of Energy is directing

The photo, top right, shows the amount of roof covered by collectors in the Arkla model sun-cooled home described in the accompanying text. The system provides about 75 percent of both cooling and heating needs. The photo at right shows the front of the same house to be a typical-looking residence, except for its extra-large garage, where solar-energy equipment is located.

This is the heat-cooling system as it is installed in the Arkla garage. At the left is the air-conditioner chiller. At the right are the system tanks. Above right is the auxiliary boiler that comes into action when solar energy is insufficient. Controls, heat exchangers, and so on, are behind the basic units shown. Arkla "packages" the unit on a skid, the unit ready for use.

a great deal of its efforts these days toward the development of solar energy systems that both heat and cool. With so much interest in solar cooling, there is no doubt that cooling will soon become as practical as heating.

The key is the development of equipment that requires less heat in order to cool. Experimental units have required that water first be heated to at least 210°F to achieve the required results. By adding a solution pump to replace the natural thermal cycle that has always been an integral part of heat-cooling systems, and by increasing the heat-transfer surfaces, the temperature requirement has been reduced to 195°F. Further development could reduce the requirement to 170°F or less.

The drawing on the next page shows the flow of water through the Arkla system. During the summer season, solar-heated water flows from the collector panels to the hot-water storage tanks. This hot water energizes the absorption chiller. The chilled water then flows to the fan-coil unit which contains a blower and a "cold exchanger." Air blowing over the exchanger coil is cooled before it is delivered into living areas.

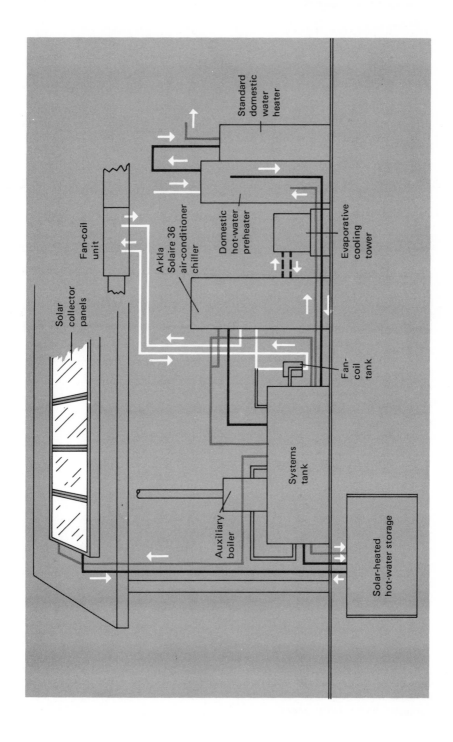

Standard domestic water heater

Fan-coil unit

Solar collector panels

Arkla Solaire 36 air-conditioner chiller

Domestic hot-water preheater

Evaporative cooling tower

Fan-coil tank

Systems tank

Auxiliary boiler

Solar-heated hot-water storage

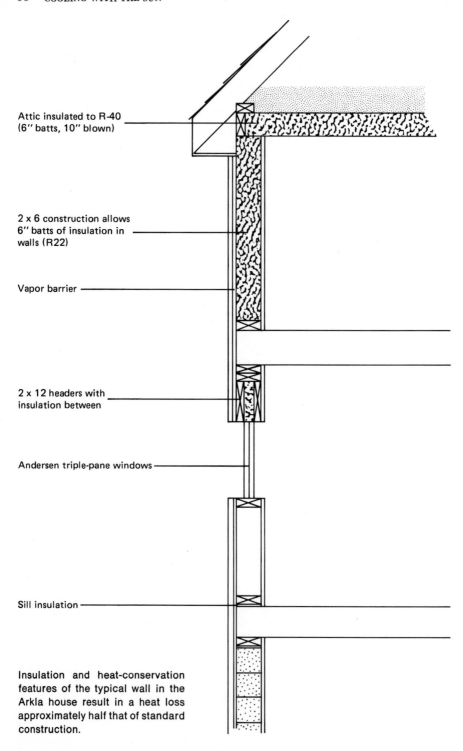

Attic insulated to R-40
(6" batts, 10" blown)

2 x 6 construction allows
6" batts of insulation in
walls (R22)

Vapor barrier

2 x 12 headers with
insulation between

Andersen triple-pane windows

Sill insulation

Insulation and heat-conservation
features of the typical wall in the
Arkla house result in a heat loss
approximately half that of standard
construction.

Another vital factor in solar cooling is house construction. The Arkla demonstration home was designed and constructed for maximum conservation of energy, and heat loss is approximately half that of what might be called a standard home.

There are polystyrene-foam panels under the concrete slab and around the edges to control movement of heat. The walls are built with 2×6 studs, instead of 2×4. This allows the use of greater thicknesses of insulation.

Windows throughout the house are triple-paned glass. Special insulation techniques are used around the windows. Throughout, every possible step was taken to reduce heat loss during the winter and heat gain during the summer.

As all of this indicates, a high degree of architectural attention must be paid to heat control in a house that will use solar heat efficiently for the same degree of cooling that can be expected from electric or fuel-burning air conditioners.

9 | How to Heat Swimming Pools

WITHOUT SOME SORT of heating system, most homeowners with a swimming pool get less use from the pool than they would like. The water is slow to warm up in the spring, and it turns cold too early in the fall. In many climates, the pool can drop below the comfort level overnight and then take until early afternoon to warm up again.

To correct this shortcoming, many pools are equipped with heating systems that keep the water up to the comfort-and-fun level. Such systems are relatively simple. Almost every swimming pool has—or should have—a circulating system which runs the water through filtering and purifying equipment. Since the water is already in motion, it is a simple matter to link a heating element into the circulation, to bring up the temperature.

Fuel-burning heaters are in use in many elaborate pool installations, but the cost of required fuel is enough to take a lot of the enjoyment out of swimming and diving for the homeowner. In fact, conservation and anti-pollution measures in some areas prohibit use of fuels for pool warming.

For these reasons, solar-energy pool heat is the ideal answer. It can be installed on the roof of a poolside building. It can be hooked into the regular circulating system. The solar heater might cost about twice as much as the one that burns regular fuel. But once it is in place, the fuel cost is ended, and the savings start paying for the equipment.

POOL HEAT COLLECTOR CAPACITY. The solar-heat collector designed to heat domestic water must be capable of warming water to around 150°F —perhaps with backup from a fuel-burning heater. On the other hand, the collector for heating swimming pools needs to warm the water only to temperatures less than 100°F. In addition, the collector gets help when the pool picks up warmth directly from bright sunlight and warm air.

As a result, the collector can be much smaller than that intended for residential use, and it rarely, if ever, needs backup heat except in bad weather. On many sunny days, it will do the job without the need for excessive insulation, glazing over the top, or insulation on the pipe runs that

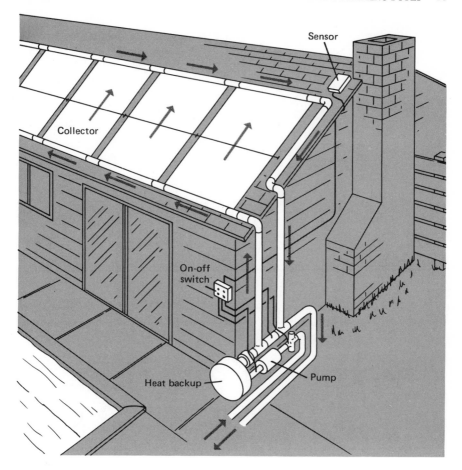

Typical delivery of solar heat to a swimming pool is shown in this drawing. The pump delivers the water through the heat backup to the collector where it is warmed before it is returned to the pool. A sensor and on-off switch control the circulation. Water is sent to the collectors only when solar heat is available. In its circulation, the water goes through the pool's regular filter-cleansing system.

feed water into the circulation. However, these features are assets because of the extra efficiency they produce—making smaller collection area possible, usually at smaller cost.

Orientation of the collector is often simple also. A poolside building can be placed so that its roof pitch catches the best sunlight exposure. When a building is not feasible, the collectors can be mounted at ground level, very inconspicuously, often shielded from view, but not shaded by shrubs. It is wise to place the collector as low as possible to reduce the amount of pressure required to force water through the system. In some cases, the col-

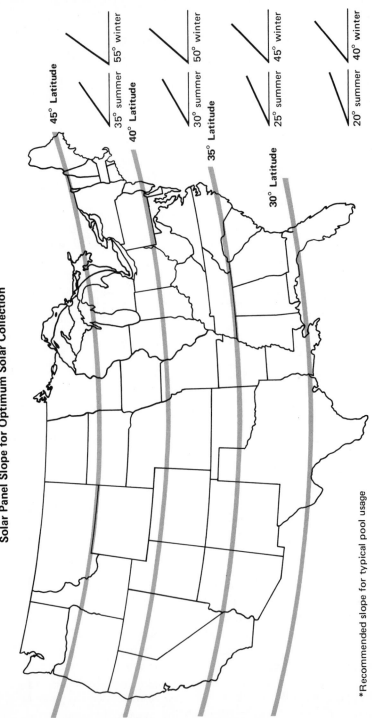

Solar Panel Slope for Optimum Solar Collection

45° Latitude

40° Latitude

35° Latitude

30° Latitude

35° summer   55° winter

30° summer   50° winter

25° summer   45° winter

20° summer   40° winter

*Recommended slope for typical pool usage

lector may drain during periods when the pool temperature is high enough so that no warming is needed. When this is the case, the lower collectors require less pumping power to refill the collector. Once the circuit is filled, of course, the syphon principle comes into effect, reducing the power needed to move the water.

The size of the collector is determined by the extent to which you expect it to increase the use of the pool—both during a given day and during the entire season. If the objective is simply to get the pool a bit warmer during the day, a small efficient collector will suffice. If you want to extend the swimming season, greater size is required.

Suppose the pool-use period in your backyard is three months. If you install a collector that is approximately half the size of the pool, you can count on a five-month swimming season.

TYPES OF SOLAR COLLECTORS. Although there are many collectors available for heating a pool, they represent only a few major types, as described below:

Plastic units. Among the simplest of all solar collectors to install are those made of a plastic such as DuPont's Hypalon. An example is the collector made by Northrup. It handles like a sheet of plastic, except that it is double,

Collector units for pool warming often consist of double layers of sheet plastic with passageways between the sheets for water circulation. The black plastic of this Fafco unit collects the heat. Such collector units are lightweight and easy for the do-it-yourselfer to install.

The collectors here are mounted on the southerly side of a peaked-roof wing of the pool house.

This poolside structure supports the collectors, while offering storage underneath and a flat vertical wall on the backside that serves as the backboard for a handball court. (Designed by W. David Houser)

and there are channels between the layers for water to move through. The circulator sends the water up to the top of the collector unit. Gravity moves it down through the channels. In the process, the water picks up heat. The plastic is black, making no treatment necessary to provide heat absorption. These units are installed simply by placing them on the slanting roof, where they are fastened with grommets. Plastic tubing (1½-inch or 2-inch PVC) carries the water up and back down to the pool. The collector units come in 8×8, 8×12, and 8×16 foot sizes, representing 64, 96, and 128 square feet.

Another lightweight collector, produced by Fafco, uses the circulator pressure to move water through the black-plastic tube sheets.

Plastic tube units. Another type of collector is composed of 1½-inch black-plastic tube laid out in serpentine parallel runs, with U connections at the ends, feeding each run into the next. The units may be just about any length, depending on space and requirements. Since there are nine runs per unit, a 10-foot unit would provide a cubic water capacity equal to the capacity of 90 feet of tubing—with water being heated as it moves slowly through

Collectors for this glass-enclosed pool and the house itself are installed in a poolside wing.

This system of collectors from Alcoa is mounted at quite a flat angle, which keeps it below the fence level, fairly well out of sight. Flat angles require a somewhat larger collector area.

the system. The tubing used by Aquasolar, Inc., for the collector is rigid acrylonitrile-butadiene-styrene, a material that will last almost indefinitely. It is relatively heavy and may require more support than a roof provides without reinforcing.

Copper tubing. A typical copper collector produced by Revere follows the design concept shown in Chapter 5. A grid of copper tubing, affixed to a metal sheet, collects the heat and delivers it. The sheet is aluminum and the copper tubing is held in place by spring clips. It connects to the circulator through ¾-inch copper tubes. The weight of each 36×96-inch unit (the standard size) is 36 pounds. Copper-and-aluminum collectors are also made by other manufacturers, such as Sun-Grabber and General Energy Devices, and function in basically the same way.

DO-IT-YOURSELF POOL HEATER. Building a pool heater from scratch can be quite a job, if you construct your own collector. However, if you

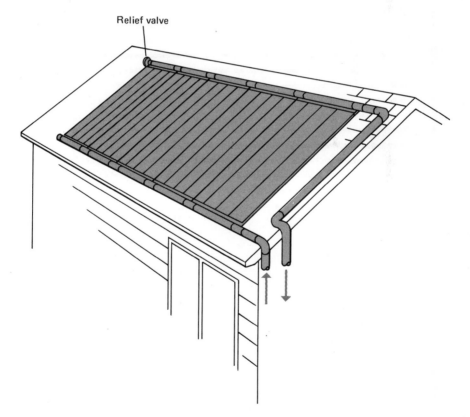

Relief valve

Simple construction is evident in this collector, by Fafco, through which water is moved by the pool circulation system. The collector comes in units which can be connected to provide the square footage needed.

buy commercial collectors in the size needed, hooking them into the circulating system presents very few problems. You will be wise to buy your components from a reliable local source, and to ask advice on the types of controls, valves, and other devices you should use to handle the weather in your locality.

If you decide to build your own pool collector, the type described in Chapter 7 should serve well. The number of such 4×8-foot units you need will be determined by the size of your pool, the weather conditions, and the length of swimming season you are after.

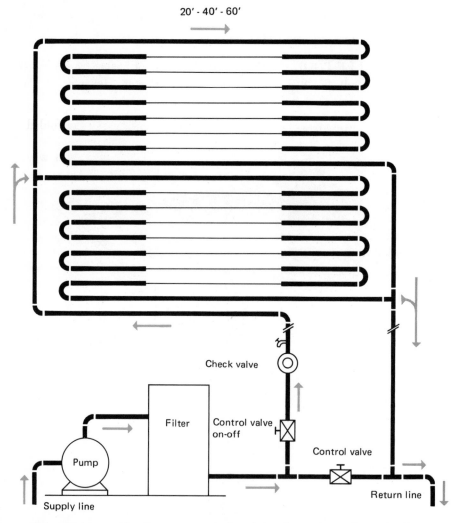

This tubular pool-heating system designed by Aquasolar utilizes the heat-collecting capabilities of black tubing in serpentine arrangement. The length of the tubing determines the heating capacity.

One of the most complete how-to manuals on pool heating is available from Copper Development Association, 405 Lexington Avenue, New York, NY 10017. However, if your do-it-yourself skills are average or better, you should be able to engineer your own system, using the techniques covered in this book.

Here are some of the basic factors you should consider:

• When a pool heater is to be used only during the normal summer season, and when the amount of warming required is relatively small, a glass cover on the collector may not be necessary. In fact, it may reduce efficiency somewhat by reflecting some of the sun's heat rays. However, if you intend to keep the pool warm well into the fall and put it back into use early in the spring, the glass cover will help increase the temperature of the warming unit.

• If you are counting on a prolonged season, you must figure on backup, using gas or propane or another fuel. In addition, a floating "lid" for the pool may be necessary, to prevent loss of warmth into the cool night air. Floating a plastic film or a cover of polystyrene foam reduces heat loss and also eliminates the cooling effect of evaporation. The cover can be folded or pulled off when the pool is in use.

• If you are putting up a pool house, you can design it in such a way that the solar collector doubles as the roof of the house. This, of course, reduces the investment chargeable to the collector.

• If your collector will be without glazing—and thus exposed to the weather—you can provide a long-life black coating by using a sealer intended for black-top driveways. Do not confuse this material with a material intended for *coating and filling*. Rather, it is the light-absorbing black and the long life of the sealer you are after.

10 | Making a Liquid Collector

THE MOST IMPORTANT ELEMENT in any solar-heat system is the collector. The components of a liquid collector are so simple that you can build the unit yourself. It can be made entirely of materials from the local lumberyard and plumbing supply house. Or you can use some special components available only from solar energy equipment suppliers. Either way, the tasks are no more difficult than those of simple plumbing and carpentry. (In some cases, you may be able to buy collector units knocked down; all you do is assemble the pieces.)

One thing is certain: Except for the most sophisticated molded plastic collectors, none of them are out of reach for the do-it-yourselfer with the tools, the time, and the technical ability. (Before reading farther, review the brief description of construction steps presented in Chapter 7. Much of the following material is an elaboration of those steps.)

MATERIALS TO WORK WITH. The most readily available and easily worked tubing materials are plastic and copper. Steel pipe is heavy, difficult to cut, and hard to "thread" for joining. Copper and plastic tubing do not require threaded joints, and they are easy to cut to length—an important factor when many pieces must be cut.

Plastic tubing comes in rigid, flexible, and semi-flexible forms, which makes it easy to handle. Also, being black, it is heat absorbent. Be sure you use only *heat-resistant plastic* that is intended for carrying hot water; some of the tubing intended for cold water might fall apart when heated to the levels a good collector can reach.

Here are the types of plastic tubing that can handle special requirements in solar energy systems:

Polyethylene. This is used only for cold-water applications. It is flexible and easy to handle, and it comes in any length you may need. Dealers normally stock it in coils as long as 400 feet, in diameters ranging from ½-inch up to 3-inch. Because polyethylene tubing is easy to handle *it can be a good choice for lines that bring cold water into the system.*

This Sun-lite glazing panel form Kalwall is an example of components the homeowner can obtain for systems he builds himself. It provides both heat-loss insulation and solar transmission. The glazing panels come in a range of sizes which cannot be altered; the collector box must be made to accept them.

Polybutylene. This is flexible also, but it can be used for hot-water transmission. The sizes range from ¼-inch to ¾-inch, in lengths up to 100 feet.

Polyvinyl chloride (PVC). This is a rigid material *intended for cold water only*. It is usually white, instead of black, as a means of differentiating between it and the next type.

Chlorinated polyvinyl chloride (CPVC). This is rigid, the same as PVC, but it is also approved for carrying hot water.

Plastic tubing is joined with plastic connectors that match the characteristics of the tube. The connectors are available in all the required Ts, Ys, elbows, and couplings. The fit between tubing and connectors is very tight. With flexible tubing, the connectors are ribbed. They slip inside the tube, forming a very tight joint. The tightness can be increased with ring clamps that tighten by means of a screw, or with spring clamps.

With rigid materials, the connectors go outside the tube, again with a very snug, tight fit. The joint is made strong and watertight with a cement or else a solvent. The cement is applied to both mating surfaces *before* they

Plastic tubing is easy to cut with a knife or—more accurately—with a backsaw in a miter box. As shown here, the plastic is being cut on a simplified version of the miter box, called a "bench hook." This is merely two pieces of wood nailed to a piece of plywood.

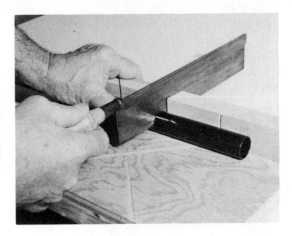

An easy way to make sure plastic joints are tight is to employ spring clips such as this one. Squeeze the two points in the jaws of a pair of pliers to slip the clamp in place, where it tightens when the pliers let go.

are slipped together. The solvent is applied *after* the two parts are put together. The solvent penetrates between the mating surfaces, softens them, and fuses them together. When they harden, the result is a "liquid weld" that is very strong and almost invariably watertight.

Plastic tubing can be cut with a sharp knife or with a workshop saw. The best saw is a fine-tooth hacksaw, used in a miter box, to produce the cleanest, truest cut. After being cut, the tubing ends should be shaved smooth with a sharp knife.

As you plan your solar energy assembly, you must keep in mind an important factor involving flexible plastic tubing joined with *connectors that slip inside the tube*. The effective water transmission size of the tubing is the inside diameter of the connector, not the designated size of the tube.

This means that the working transmission capacity of the assembly may be one size smaller than the nominal tube size. When the speed of transmission is not critical, keep in mind that the tubing contributes to the water-volume requirements by supplying storage for water that has been brought to temperature.

Copper tubing. Copper tubing is far more expensive than the plastic materials, but it provides better service in some situations—often justifying the cost difference. For instance, when the tubing must carry part of the heat transmission load as well as the liquid transmission, copper is vastly superior. There are also, certain joinery situations in which copper will work and plastic won't. This occurs, for example, when soldering tubing to the sheet material of the collector.

However, it is easy to convert from copper to plastic, using special fittings. When performance allows and when economics are important, copper and plastic can team up. For instance, you might use copper for the collector, with plastic for transmission of the fluid in and out of the collector.

Copper comes in a heavy form, which must be joined with threaded connectors, the same as steel pipe. It is generally intended for underground use. There is no need for this heavy copper in a solar energy system since there is rarely a tremendous pressure load, and there is very little corrosion. Therefore, the lightweight, thin-wall copper tubing should always be your choice.

Joinery is with solder, an easy material to use, even for the beginner. Use rosin-core solder labeled 50-50 for joining tubing. For fastening tubing to sheet metal, as in the collector, use acid-core, which is intended for heavier

Copper fittings, as well as the tubing itself, come in two thicknesses. The easiest to work with are the thin fittings shown at right.

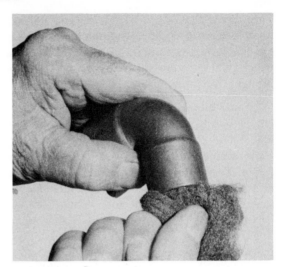

Twisting the tubing in a handful of steelwool produces the clean, shiny surface required for a good, soldered joint. Right, the steelwool must be applied inside the fitting, also, so that both joining surfaces are clean enough.

work. Actually, when the amount of soldering is great, it is best to use a solid-core material, supplying the flux as a separate operation. Specific instructions come with the solder and with the flux.

SOLDERING TECHNIQUES. Clean metal, proper fit, fluxing, and heating are the basics of soldering for simple solar energy projects.

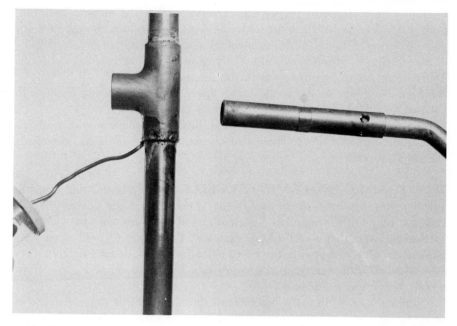

The best soldered joint in copper tubing results from holding the torch on the opposite side of the fitting. Heated, it draws the solder into the joint. Gradually work around the fitting until the solder bead is visible all around. Note that the job can be done with the heat above the joint, since the heat will draw the solder upward as well as downward.

- The mating surfaces must be clean—shining bright. Medium-grade steel wool gives you this clean surface most easily. Use it on the outside of the tube and on the inside of the fitting.
- Apply paste flux to both surfaces before you fit them together, if paste is your choice. If you are using liquid flux, slip the parts together and flow the flux into the joint.
- Heat the mating parts with a torch to a *temperature that will melt the solder. It is extremely important that the metal itself melt the solder*—not the heat from the torch. This assures that the solder will be drawn into the joint by capillary action, producing the strongest, tightest joint possible.
- Keep the torch or iron ahead of the solder, as you work along or around the joint. The molten solder tends to flow toward the heat. You can, therefore, watch the flow and the penetration of the solder to make sure you are getting a good, tight joint.

Soldering is simplest with a propane torch, such as the Bernz-O-Matic. The small-tip flame is applied directly to the metals being joined, heating them quickly to a temperature that will melt the solder and produce a good joint. A recent innovation for such torches is Mapp gas, considered by some operators to be superior to propane. Do not expect the electric soldering guns, extremely useful for light soldering work, to produce enough heat for easy soldering of metal tubes, connectors, and sheets.

A few minutes of practice will make you an expert with solder and torch. Don't be afraid to experiment with tubing and fittings that will be part of the final assembly. They can be taken apart easily by heating them with the torch, so they can be reused in the final assembly.

When a joint is finished and has cooled, flush it thoroughly with water to remove the flux chemicals. There is a chance of corrosion if the chemicals are not removed.

HOW TO MAKE AN ALL-METAL COLLECTOR. For maximum heat absorption from the rays of the sun, a metal collector is the answer. Metals conduct heat with tremendous efficiency, and they are able to withstand extremes of heat that a well-engineered, well-built collector will absorb.

As noted above, copper is the best choice for metal, despite its cost. It is easy to work with. And you can count on a life of 20 years or more from a collector's copper elements.

Aluminum is used in many commercial systems, and it is the easiest metal of all to cut and bend. However, it is difficult to solder, even though there are aluminum solders. The problem is that the heat from the torch may melt the aluminum as well as the solder, since their melting points are nearly the same. For that reason, aluminum sheet becomes the best choice mainly when the tubing is plastic, fastened to the sheet with clips.

The collector plate. The size of a homemade solar collector is dictated by the standard 4×8-foot size of exterior plywood, since plywood forms the

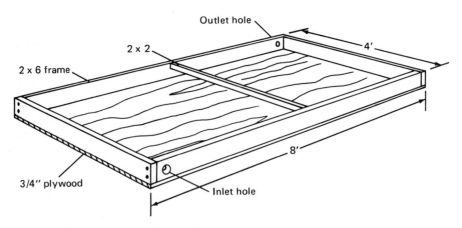

These are the dimensions and materials for a simple, 4x8-foot box to house the solar collector. The size was chosen because of the availability of 4x8 materials. Modify it if your choice of materials dictates. Use screws for all joints, and caulk them to ensure watertightness.

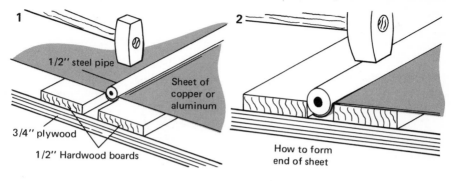

1

1/2" steel pipe

Sheet of copper or aluminum

3/4" plywood

1/2" Hardwood boards

2

How to form end of sheet

3

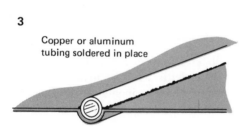

Copper or aluminum tubing soldered in place

Details of the grooving jig are shown here. The hardwood boards should be 4-feet long, ½-inch thick, and nailed securely to the sheet of ¾-inch plywood. The half-inch steel pipe is hammered down to form the groove. Space between the hardwood pieces should be about ⅛-inch wider than the outside diameter of the tubing to be used.

base of the entire unit. Therefore, the first step in making a collector is to put together the "box" it will go in. You start by making a frame of preservative-treated 2×6s that measures, outside, exactly 4×8 feet. Using nails or screws, with a mastic sealant, fasten a 4×8 sheet of ¾-inch plywood to the frame of 2×6s. From then on, dimensions for the sheet and the grid are determined by the *inside dimensions* of the box. This means that you must cut about 6 inches off the edge of the 4-foot-wide metal sheet that will become the collector. The length is also determined by the size of the box, but it must be established later, as explained below.

The collector plate consists of the sheet plus the tubing that carries the heat-gathering liquid. The tubing may be on the top of the sheet, on the bottom of the sheet, or nestled into grooves formed in the sheet. To ensure heat transfer through plastic tubing, the inlaid version is a must. But copper tubing is really the best because of its high conductance.

You can put the required grooves in metal sheet using the jig shown in the accompanying drawing. Fasten securely two 4-foot lengths of ½-inch-thick hardwood to a piece of ¾-inch plywood. The space between the two strips of hardwood should be about ⅛-inch wider than the outside diameter of the tubing. Position the sheet carefully over the slot between the hardwood strips, and place the pipe on top of the sheet. Hammer the pipe into the space, forming a groove in the sheet. As the metal is forced down, the

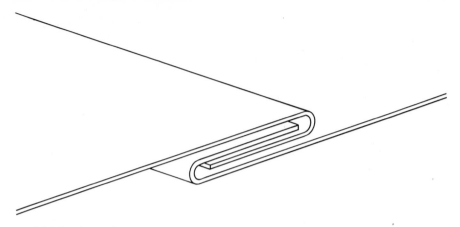

Join aluminum sheets together by bending a U in the edge of each, interlocking the U's, then hammering them tight with a rubber mallet. The resultant joint will transfer heat without the need for soldering.

flat area of the sheet on both sides will tend to rise. Hold the steel pipe down, and tap along both sides of the sheet with a rubber mallet to make the bend smooth and sharp. Repeat this every eight inches to produce 10 grooves across the sheet plus a half-groove at each end, to accept the lengths of tubing that will be fastened there.

The grooves thus formed will be about the right size to accept ½-inch copper tubing, although it may be necessary to squeeze them together slightly for a snug fit as you solder.

Important: The preceding operation will be easy with aluminum sheet, or with copper. Don't try it with galvanized sheet, which is a bit too stiff and too thick to bend properly.

Each groove you make in this operation will reduce the effective length of the sheet. An 8-foot sheet will close accordion-fashion to about 6½ feet. Therefore, in order to end up with a collector sheet that is the right length —about 90 inches—you will have to add to the length of the sheet. Do so by using one of the following techniques:

• Working with copper, lap the adjoining sheets about ¾ inch and clamp them in place. Use copper rivets every 6 or 8 inches to hold the splice tight. Then run a bead of solder along the edge of the splice, top and bottom.

• The method of joining aluminum sheets is shown in the accompanying drawing. Usually it provides sufficient metal-to-metal contact so that soldering is not necessary.

Making the fluid-carrying grid. The technique involved in putting together a grid of copper or of plastic are basically the same, except that liquid welding is used with plastic and regular hot soldering is used with copper. The simplest method is that outlined in Chapter 7 and covered in detail as follows:

Cutting copper tubing is quick and easy with this tube cutter sold at plumbing supply outlets or hardware stores. Rotate the tool around the tube. The wheel makes a cut. Tighten the screw and make another turn. Continue this process until the cut is complete.

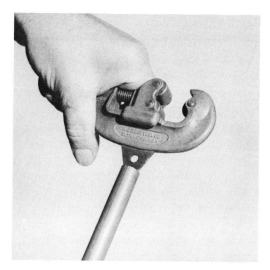

After the tube is cut, ream out the burr inside, caused by the cutting wheel. The sharp V-shaped cutter on the tool does the reaming job. This cuts down on friction, letting the liquid move more readily.

• Cut one length of ½-inch tubing for each of the grooves plus one for each half groove at the ends. These pieces should be about 1½ inches longer than the width of the grooved sheet.

• Fasten ½×¾×¾-inch Ts to the end of each length of ½-inch tube. Make sure that they are absolutely parallel—easiest to do if you work on a perfectly flat, plane surface.

• Lay one T-tube-T unit in the first groove and one in the second. Measure from the lip of one to the lip of the other. Add one inch, and cut a piece of ¾-inch tubing to that length.

Important: Be sure to use steel wool to polish the ends of the tubing and the inside of the Ts. Also, ream the burr out of the ends of the tubes.

• Solder this piece of ¾-inch tubing in place.

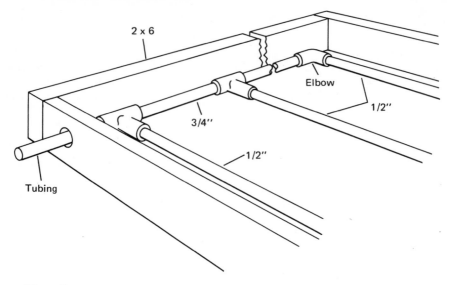

The collector units are interconnected with a short length of tubing that passes through the 2x6 frame. At the ends of the grid, the connector is an elbow.

• Move to the other end of this pair of tubes and repeat the joining operation.

• Put the next length of ½-inch tube in place. Measure for the length of the ¾-inch piece. Steelwool, ream, and solder. Do the other end.

• Repeat the process above for each of the lengths. You end up with a grid that exactly fits the sheet-metal plate, and fits inside the collector box with a little space all around. The next step is to solder the tubing to the plate in the grooves. Apply pressure to bring the tubing and groove into contact. Aim the soldering torch at the joint, and run a fillet of solder along the tube on both sides. When this soldering is done, you have an assembly of heat-conducting metal that is very close to solid—up, down, and across.

Working with plastic tube. If you decide to do the job with plastic tube, the basic procedures are the same as with copper. These are the differences:

• Modify the thickness of the two hardwood strips and the spacing between them to accommodate the actual size of the plastic tubing. The thickness should be a little more than *half the outside diameter* of the tubing. The spacing should be about an eighth of an inch wider than the outside diameter. This will give you grooves into which the plastic tubing will make a good fit.

• After the Ts have been fastened permanently to the ends of the vertical lengths, lay them in the grooves and cut the short, horizontal pieces. Do not apply the binding solder yet.

• Drill small holes through the sheet on opposite sides of the vertical lengths, about every 10 inches.

• Form inverted Us of aluminum wire and slip them over the tubing, through the holes. Twist them in back, to hold the tubing tight in the grooves.

Now apply the solvent to the Ts and short lengths across the top and bottom. Whether you are working with copper or plastic, you have a grid which exactly fits the grooved sheet metal plate.

As it now stands, the grid is open at all four corners. It can be connected with tubing to another grid beside it—and that one to still another—and on, until the total required collector area is achieved. To make these connections, you will use short lengths of tubing that run through matching holes inside 2×6s top and bottom. Take the required measurements to determine the positions for these holes and drill them with a bit that gives the tubing a close fit—but not too tight.

Collector insulation. To collect the amount of heat required for home heating, you need water temperatures that are higher than what you would need for domestic water heating alone. So you must prevent loss of heat from the collector plate. Here you need more insulation. To accommodate this insulation, the collector pan is made of 2×6s, instead of the 2×4s that are adequate for domestic water heating, as covered in Chapter 7. Using 2×6s, you have a pan 5½ inches deep, giving you plenty of room for a 3½-inch batt of mineral wool.

Use the batts that have aluminum foil on one side—and put them in the pan foil-side-up. This reflective surface increases the heat-gathering capacity of the collector. Staple the edges of the batts to the 2×6s.

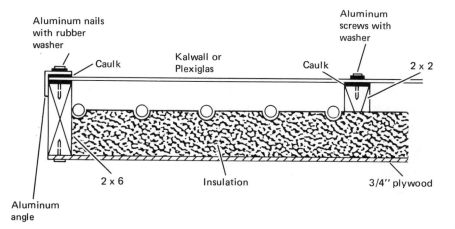

Plastic sheet or a product such as Kalwall Sun-Lite can be installed as shown here. Cut the sheet to size, and lay it in a bead of caulk on the 2x6 frame. Run a bead of caulk around the edge of the sheet. Lay 1½-inch aluminum angle all around, fastened with aluminum nails and rubber washers.

The collector plate can now be laid in place, on top of the insulation. There is no need for any other support, unless the unit is to be installed vertically. In that case, cleats should be nailed to the inside faces of the 2×6s, to prevent the plate from tilting forward.

After the collector plate is in place, cut a length of 2×2 to fit across the inside of the box. Run screws through the 2×6s into the ends of this 2×2, holding it flush with the top edges of the 2×6s. The purpose of this cross member is to support the glazing in the middle, as covered later in this chapter.

Connecting the plates. More than one—even several—collectors will be needed to handle the required heat load. They must be connected together side by side. To do this, you must cut short lengths of tubing that will reach from the T in one box to the T in the next, and so on. Establish the length of these short connecting pieces by laying two collectors side by side. Measure from the end of one T to the end of the other. Add one inch, for insertion of tubing into the Ts. Technically, they should all be the same length, but there may be slight differences. These lengths, inserted across the top and across the bottom, constitute a horizontal run the full length of the combined units, when they are all linked together.

Soldering, or cementing, these pieces in place will come after the units are mounted in place. Thus, only one 4×8 unit will have to be handled at a time.

Important: If you have determined the number of units you will need, use an L instead of a T in the lower corner of the unit opposite the intake of liquid, and in the corner of the unit opposite the outflow of liquid. If you are unsure how many units you will need, you can assemble all the units to test for total requirements. In this case you can block off the ends of the unconnected Ts, using standard plugs or caps.

When the collector units are completed, put them in place on the support, mounted at the proper angle. Then anchor the units by whatever means the situation requires.

Insert the short connecting lengths and solder or cement them in place. Run four 3-inch No. 12 screws, evenly spaced, through mating 2×6s. This will give you the total collector, in place and ready for painting.

For the tubing and plates, you need a flat, black paint that will withstand temperatures as high as 400°F. Ask your paint dealer for a paint intended for barbecues. Sapolin makes such a paint. Or you can check with your solar heating supply outlet for the paint he recommends.

Use a spray gun to apply this flat, black paint. If you don't have one, a rental outlet will probably have the outfit you need. Spraying is the only method that will ensure complete and thorough coverage of absorbing surfaces.

Glazing the collector. You have several choices of glazing material that will increase the collector's efficiency. The covering may be glass, it

Plastic sheet is easy to work with, making the glazed cover. It can be cut with a sharp scriber. After several strokes across the material, place it over a table or bench edge and press downward to break it.

may be plastic, or it may be one of the special materials made specifically for use on solar collectors. An example is a product called Kalwall Sun-Lite, which is available from solar-energy suppliers.

It is advisable—even essential—to provide the glazing for the collector in a form that is removable, in case repairs or modifications inside are needed, some day. As suggested in Chapter 7, you can put together a covering using window-framing materials. If you do, the most functional form would be a pair of 4×4-foot units, that would join over the crossmember of the collector frame. That way, the pieces of glass would be only 4×4 feet. The glass should be shatterproof.

This photo from Solar Energy Products shows the types of components that may be included in a kit. Collectors, controls, mounting elements, and couplings are shown, leaving only pipe runs to be
purchased locally as required.

If you decide on a plastic or the Kalwall material, you can use a sheet
the full 4×8 size. Window-framing is not necessary. These materials can
be fastened to the edges of the 2×6s, as shown in the drawing, providing
a tight joint, even though the sheet can be removed if necessary.

Some experts in solar energy collection recommend double-glazing, for
added insulation. Two sheets of glass or plastic are used, separated by
molding. If you assemble a double-glazed cover, be sure that the separa-
tion is great enough so that the upper sheet won't sag into contact with
the lower sheet—killing the insulating value of the dead air. Single or double glazed, the cover must be sealed with caulk to prevent heat loss and to
keep moisture out.

Hooking up the system. With your solar collector in place, all that remains is to connect the collector to the house system. The several types of
heat utilization are covered in Chapter 5. The exact hookup will depend on
the facilities available or those you may install. As the diagrams in Chapter
5 show, the heated liquid is pumped into the home's entire hot-water heating system or simply to the domestic hot-water system.

The liquid moves from the collector to the system through standard
plumbing lines, which can be metal or plastic. Be sure to check local building codes for any regulations that dictate which plumbing materials are
permitted.

If the collector is mounted on the roof, drill holes through the roof to
admit the runs to and from the unit. Use caulk to make these holes weather
proof. If the collector is mounted on a separate building or elsewhere outside the house, make the runs underground, insulating the pipes with special material intended for such exposure. Entry and exit will most often
be through basement walls, in this case, through holes made into the basement or crawl space.

Inside the house, you may have to modify systems, or even install new
ones. Check with local plumbing supply outlets and especially with solar
energy specialists for the drains, check-valves, thermostatic controls, heat
exchangers, storage tanks, and other elements the system requires.

11 | Making a Hot-Air Collector

A GREAT DEAL more research and development has gone into solar liquid systems than into air systems. Less than half of the solar-heated houses today are engineered to use solar-heated air. However, it's often easier to heat air to an adequate temperature than water. Besides, it's simpler and less expensive to deliver heated air to points of use.

Solar-industry leaders that have built their position with liquid systems are now experimenting with air. But the ultimate question is not, which system is better? Rather, you should determine which system better meets the requirements of your own situation.

Besides simplicity and economy, another major advantage of air systems is that they pose no threat of damage due to leaking or freezing. The bin, full of heated stones, doesn't need to be waterproof. Perhaps of greatest importance, ducts and collectors for air systems can be made of aluminum or steel, materials that are less expensive than copper, which is recommended most frequently for liquid systems.

The main disadvantage of air is that air cannot hold or transport nearly as much heat as equal volumes of water can. This makes a difference in the size of heat-storage facilities. The tank you might use to store liquid heat would occupy much less space than the stone bin used for hot air.

Another consideration is the energy required to move air through the ducts. The larger the transport ducts, the less energy is required—but the larger the ducts, the more they cost. Nevertheless, when the space inside walls and beneath floors is great enough to allow the installation of adequate ducts, the cost to move the air is a minor factor.

From the do-it-yourself standpoint, the hot-air method has the advantage of requiring no great plumbing knowledge and skills. If the air system involves a heat exchanger to heat domestic water, you will need plumbing methods and materials for the connection. Other than that, the hookup requires only the joining of ductwork that slips together by means of simple techniques.

Air systems require no soldering. Everything can be assembled with well-fitting slip joints, and then sealed and covered by asbestos tape that is very easy to apply. At certain points in the air distribution system you may find it necessary to rivet some slip joints to ensure against stress that might pull apart a joint bonded only with the asbestos tape. When riveting is necessary, the "Pop" Rivet tool makes the job quick and easy.

Another important advantage of an air system is the amount of air that will move *by natural convection.* You can position a "rotation engineered" collector in such a way that air is continuously drawn in at the bottom and carried to the top by convection. When it loses temperature (warming its surroundings) it falls and is recirculated. Although convection is not a tremendous force, it is strong enough to move a lot of air, since the ducts form ample channels for circulation. Whenever the air must be moved great distances and whenever there are many angles, joints, and other sources of friction, a low-power fan will augment the convection, bringing circulation up to the required level.

BUILDING AN AIR-HEAT COLLECTOR. Maximum metal-to-air contact is vital for top efficiency of a collector that heats air. In some commercial collectors, this is provided by sheets of metal to which metal fins are attached the full length of the sheet. Heat from the sun is absorbed by the sheet and conducted to the fins. The total metal-to-air surface, therefore, is the total area of the sheet plus the area of both sides of the fins.

The assembly of sheet and fins is a difficult metal-joining process that is too much work for the average do-it-yourselfer. However, a solar-heat supplier may be able to supply you with sheets that you can build into your collectors. Otherwise, here is an extremely practical alternative:

Metal roofing collector sheet. Your building-supply dealer can provide a metal roofing material that has V-grooves running the length of the sheets, spaced several inches apart. The V-groove roofing comes in aluminum or galvanized steel. You will find aluminum lighter to handle and easier to work with.

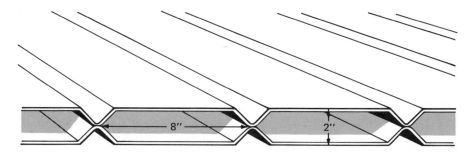

V-grooved roofing can be fabricated as shown here into an excellent collector plate for solar air heating. The sheets are fastened together with rivets so that the tips of the Vs meet. The result is a series of side-by-side ducts about 2 inches thick and 8 inches wide through which the air passes. Painted flat black, the collector transmits solar heat to the air as it moves through the ducts.

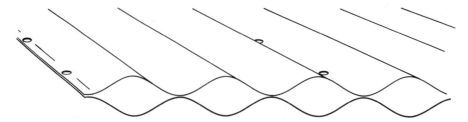

Corrugated siding can be joined as shown here, to form tubes for the flow of air through the solar collector. Rivets hold the sheets together. Metal-to-air contact is excellent. For best collection and heat transfer, the upper surface should be painted flat black.

To make a collector of these sheets, fasten two of them together as shown in the accompanying drawing. Rivets every foot or so along the grooves will hold the sheets together. You needn't be concerned about possible leaks around the rivets, since the hot-air collector system tolerates minor leaks. Should the size of the collector call for a sheet larger than available V-groove roofing, splicing is simple, merely by overlapping the grooves at the edges.

Corrugated siding collector sheet. Another standard building material that can be used for a collector is ordinary corrugated siding. It comes in aluminum or galvanized steel, in widths narrower than the collector should be. Splicing the material to make the required width is a simple matter of overlapping the edges—just as they would overlap if you were putting them on the wall of a building.

To make the collector, place one unit of corrugated material over the other so that the "down-dip" of the upper piece rests on the rise of the lower piece. Use rivets along the edge and every foot or so in every fourth dip. (See the drawing.)

The resulting collector sheet consists of several tube-like channels through which the air travels. It does not have quite as much air space as the one made of V-groove roofing, described earlier, but it has more metal-to-air contact, making higher temperatures possible.

Building the collector housing. Here's what's involved in building a simple do-it-yourself hot-air collector:

• Air enters the unit at the bottom through a duct leading into a chamber located below the collector sheet. The chamber feeds air into the lower end of the tubes or ducts of the collector plate.

• Air moves up through the collector plate, picking up heat as it goes.

• At the upper end of the plate, the air enters another chamber, from which it is delivered to the storage bin, via standard ductwork.

• From the bin, it goes to the heat distribution system of the house. In

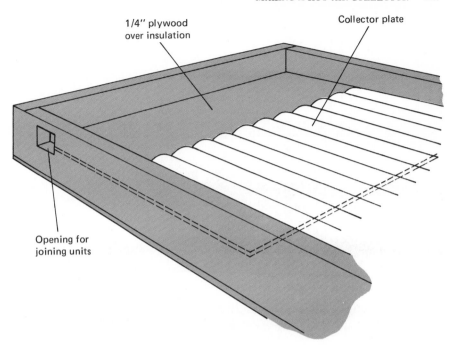

1/4" plywood
over insulation

Collector plate

Opening for
joining units

The chambers at the top and bottom of the collectors must be joined, side by
side. Cut holes in the sides of the frame, positioned identically, so that the
air can pass through when the units are mounted.

some cases, the heated air may pass through a heat exchanger that produces
domestic hot water. (In more complicated systems, the heated air may re-
circulate through the heater, entering at the bottom and making another
run through the collector plate.)

Many of the procedures involved in making the hot-air collector housing
are the same as those used in making the liquid system, covered in Chapter 10. So read through that chapter for methods that will apply to construction of the hot-air collector.

The first step in building the collector housing is to put together the
frame. Here you must answer these questions: Would it be simpler to
make the frame to fit the collector plate that results from efficient assembly
of the plate materials? Or, would it be simpler to adjust the size of the plate
to fit inside a frame made of standard 4×8-foot materials?

As you make the decision, keep in mind that the plate can touch the sides
of the frame. At the top and bottom, however, you must leave four to six
inches of space for entry and exit of the air.

Use 2×6s to make the frame, with a sheet of ¾-inch plywood forming
the bottom. Fasten things together with screws and caulk to make the

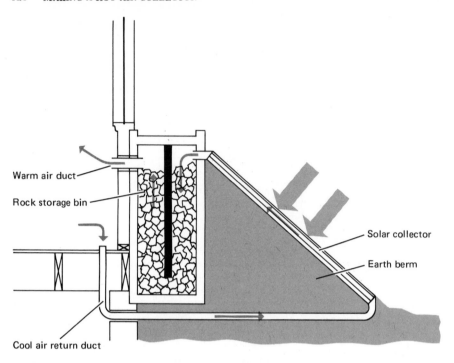

Warm air duct

Rock storage bin

Solar collector

Earth berm

Cool air return duct

One good way to mount your air-heat solar collector is on a berm outside the house, facing the right direction, at the right angle. Air circulates through the collector as shown here, picking up heat, storing it, and delivering it to the living area as needed.

frame weathertight. The resulting frame should be the same as the one that is used for liquid collectors, as described in Chapter 10.

Put 3½-inch batts of aluminum-faced glass wool insulation in the frame, aluminum side up. Lay a 12-inch strip of ¼-inch plywood across the upper and lower ends. The purpose of this strip is to provide a bottom for the chambers. Fasten it in place with brads or small cleats.

Now the collector goes in place. Adjust it so that the spaces at top and bottom are equal. Fasten it at the sides, to keep it from sliding down when the collector is mounted at the required angle.

At this point, spray the inside flat black. Use a barbecue grill paint or one intended for solar-heat collectors which you can obtain from solar-heat dealers.

Cover the collector with glass, plastic, or special solar heat materials, as covered in Chapter 10.

Joining units together. When more than one unit such as the one covered above is needed—as will surely be the case—they are joined side by side. Cut holes at the corners, making sure that they coincide, unit to unit, producing a continuous passageway for air across the combined units. This must be done top and bottom, on both sides, except for the two end units, which need holes only on the joining sides.

Make these holes by drilling through the 2×6s, then cutting out the opening with a saber saw. Keep in mind that the holes must be as large as possible, to make movement of the air free and easy.

HOOKING THE COLLECTOR TO THE SYSTEM. To hook up the collector to the heating system, a run of ducting is necessary to carry the heat out, into the storage bin, on through the system, and back to the collector for reheating. Of course, the ducting run will already be in place if you are retrofitting an existing warm-air system. If you are starting from scratch, the system should be identical to that you would use for a fuel-burning system. In fact, in most situations there will be seasonal need for a furnace as backup for the solar heat.

Thus, all the ducting requirements for hookup will be standard items, except for those that fasten the system to the collector you make yourself. These connectors may have to be formed of ducting material modified to fit the opening. The easiest method of making the actual contact will be

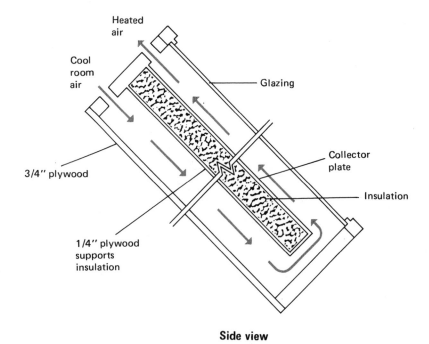

Side view

A recirculating air-heat collector works as shown in this drawing. Air enters at the top, below the insulation, falls to the chamber below and is returned to the living area. This system produces more heat from less collector area.

through flanges bent outward on the end of a piece of ducting sized to fit the opening. Roofing nails through these flanges will hold the connector in place. A little caulking will make it airtight.

It is always good practice with air-heat ducting to cover the ducts with asbestos insulation. New forms of this material are self-sticking, in dimensions to fit standard ducts. The savings in heat loss make this insulation well worth its cost and the simple labor involved in putting it around the ducts.

A ROCK-FILLED STORAGE BIN. The rock storage bin for solar-air heat should be in the basement or in a pit dug in the ground. The recommended size for a typical home is about 8×12 feet, 6 feet high. This size will hold something in the neighborhood of 15 tons of fist-size rocks.

Basement Rock Bin

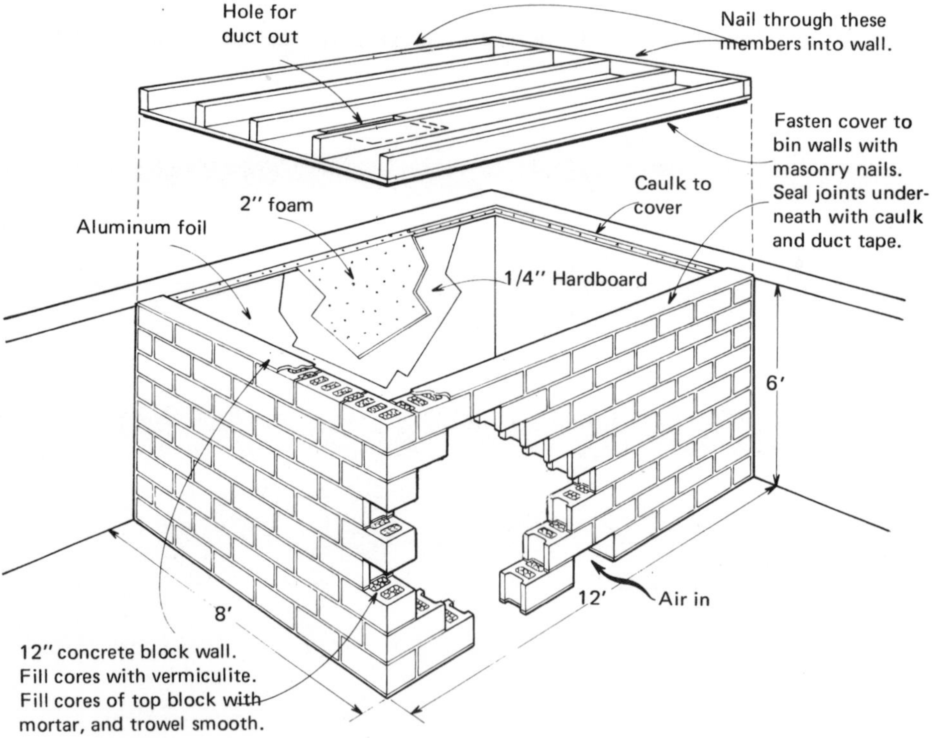

Build a rock bin as shown here. The foam-foil hardboard layer is necessary only if the original basement walls are exposed to the air. With berming outside, the insulation can be eliminated. See the text for fundamental how-to information. Fill with rocks no bigger than fist-size, no smaller than golfball size, for maximum storage efficiency.

Most logically, you should build the bin in a corner of your basement because two of the walls are already there. The other two walls (or three or four, if a corner location is not feasible) are built with concrete blocks. Some experts recommend 12-inch blocks, with the cores filled with vermiculite insulating material, to minimize heat loss through the walls. However, it may be a good idea to use 8-inch blocks, with no insulation, so that there is a deliberate heat loss into the basement—helping to keep the house warm. A compromise would be 8-inch block with insulation.

There is no need for insulation on the basement walls, if you berm the walls on the outside. The earth provides excellent resistance to heat loss, and the basement wall provides additional heat storage. In very cold climates, however, two inches of polystyrene-foam insulation may be necessary to save heat.

Construction is standard masonry, easy enough for the average do-it-yourselfer. If the block-laying job is not for you, call in a local mason, show him the accompanying drawing, and he'll have the job done in a day or so.

If the walls are not filled with insulation, one special operation is necessary. Stuff a double handful of fiberglass insulating material three or four inches down into the top of all the cement block cores in the top course. This will act as a "cork," cutting off air circulation. Pour in mortar to fill the remainder of these cores, so that the top of the masonry can be troweled smooth. If the cores are filled with insulation, leave three or four inches unfilled at the top of each core to allow for the smooth-troweled top.

In the process of laying the wall, leave out the middle block of the bottom course, on one side. This is the opening through which the solar-heated air is ducted into storage.

The cover for the bin is made of 2×4s and ¾-inch plywood, with 3½ inches of insulation between the 2×4s. When it is in place, it should rest on a heavy bead of caulk, to prevent air leakage. Caulking is necessary along the basement walls, also.

The hole for the warm-air exit duct should be in the cover on the far side from the intake duct. This is important, since it forces the air to take the longest possible route through the rocks, thereby transferring heat best.

Since the rocks in the storage bin will total about 15 tons it is advisable to build the storage bin under an existing window, so that the rocks can be dumped in easily. Be sure that the rocks are clean, free of dust and dirt. Otherwise, the moving air will gradually distribute dirt throughout the house. To wash the rocks beforehand, use a water hose. But be sure they are dry before they are dumped into the bin.

Connect the ducts into the bin and to the air system. Then the sun can start its heating job the first thing the next morning.

APPENDICES

I. Manufacturers and Distributors

II. North American Solar Incentives

Manufacturers and Distributors

This listing is derived from a similar listing compiled by the National Solar Heating and Cooling Information Center. Appearance of a manufacturer's name does not imply endorsement by Popular Science Books, nor does absence of a name indicate disapproval. Further information should be obtained by contacting the sources on upcoming pages or the National Solar Heating and Cooling Information Center, P.O. Box 1607, Rockville, MD 20850; toll free: (800) 523-2929.

GLOSSARY OF PRODUCT CODES USED

Note: These codes were devised to cover general categories of equipment and accessories. The manufacturer or distributor should be contacted for more specific product information.

APPLICATIONS
AHW: Domestic hot water
AHE: Space heating
APO: Swimming pool heating
ACO: Space cooling
  ACA: Absorption cooling
  ACD: Dessicant cooling
AHC: Heating/Cooling
AGH: Greenhouses
AMH: Mobile homes
AAG: Agriculture

COLLECTORS
CFA: Air flat plate collectors
CFL: Liquid flat plate collectors
CTU: Tubular collectors
CBL: Solar heating balloons
CCN: Concentrating collectors
CFE: Flat plate evacuated collectors
CCM: Collector components
  CMG: Glazing
  CMA: Absorber plates
  CMH: Heat transfer fluids
  CMI: Corrosion inhibitors
  CMS: Sealants
  CMM: Mounting systems
  CMT: Tracking devices
  CMF: Fresnel lenses
  CMC: Selective coatings
  CMR: Reflective surfaces
  CMP: Pumps
  CMB: Fans

SOLAR CONTROLS
COS: Complete systems
COC: Components

STORAGE
STA: Air (rock bed)
STL: Liquid
STP: Phase change
STC: Components

COMPLETE SYSTEMS
SYA: Air
SYL: Liquid
SYP: Passive
SSF: Solar furnaces
SPC: Swimming pool covers
HYB: Hybrid (active and passive)

MISCELLANEOUS
INS: Instrumentation/Measurement
HEX: Heat exchangers
HEP: Heat pumps
RCE: Rankine cycle engine
HEL: Heliostats
KIT: Do-it-yourself kits
FEA: Listed in FEA Survey of Solar Collector Manufacturers
NBS: Collectors tested according to NBS standards
LAB: Testing equipment
ASH: Tested according to ASHRAE standards

ALABAMA

Energy Engineering, Inc.
P.O. Box 1156
Tuscaloosa, AL 35401
(205) 339-5598
Product code: **STL**

Halstead and Mitchell
P.O. Box 1110
Scottsboro, AL 35768
(205) 259-1212
Product codes: **AHE   AHW   CFL
FEA**

IBM-Federal Systems Division
Research Park
Huntsville, AL 35807
(205) 837-4000
Product code: **INS**

International Solar Industries, Inc.
3107 Memorial Parkway N.W.
Huntsville, AL 35801
Product codes: **AHE   AHW   CFA
SYL**

Medtherm Corp.
P.O. Box 412
Huntsville, AL 35804
(205) 837-2000
Product code: **INS**

National Energy Systems Corp.
P.O. Box 1176
Birmingham, AL 35201
(205) 252-7726
Product codes: **AHE   AHW   APO
CFL   SYL   COS   COC   STL   ASH**

Solar Unlimited
4310 Governor's Drive
Huntsville, AL 35805
(205) 837-7340
Product codes: **HEX   AHE   AHW
APO   CFL   CCM   CMG   CMA
CMM   COS   COC   STL   SYL**

Sun Century Systems
P.O. Box 2036
Florence, AL 35630
(205) 764-0795
Product codes: **AHE   AHW   CFL
FEA   APO**

**Wolverine Tube Div./Universal
Oil Products**
P.O. Box 2202
Decatur, AL 35601
(205) 353-1310
Product code: **HEX**

ARIZONA

Arizona Aluminum
249 S. 51st Ave (Box 6736)
Phoenix. AZ 85005
(602) 269-2488
Product code: **CCM**

Arizona Engineering & Refrigeration
635 W. Commerce Ave.
Gilbert, AZ 85234
(602) 892-9050
Product codes: **AHE   AHW   APO
CFL   FEA   NBS**

Arizona Solar Enterprises
6719 E. Holly St.
Scottsdale, AZ 85257
(602) 945-7477
Product codes: **AHE   AHW   APO
CFL**

Delavan Electronics, Inc.
14605 North 73rd St.
Scottsdale, AZ 85260
(602) 948-6350
Product codes: **AHE   CCM   CMT**

Diversified Natural Resources
8025 E. Roosevelt (Suite A)
Scottsdale, AZ 85257
(602) 945-2330
Product codes: **AHC   CCN   FEA**

ENERGEX Corp.
2302 E. Magnolia St.
Phoenix, AZ 85040
(602) 267-9474
Product codes: **AHW   AHE   APO
CFL   SYL   STL   NBS**

Hansberger Refrigeration & Electric Co.
2450 8th St.
Yuma, AZ 85364
(602) 783-3331
Product codes: **AHE   AHW   CFL
FEA**

J & J Solar
7273 North Central Ave.
Phoenix, AZ 85020
(602) 956-9536
Product codes: **AHW   AHE   APO
AGH   AMH   AAG   CFL   CCM
CMA   CMH   CMM   CMC   COS
COC   STL   SYL   HEX   KIT   ASH**

Mel Kiser and Assoc.
6701 E. Kenyon Dr.
Tucson, AZ 85710

Product codes: **AHW   AHC   CCN
SYL**

Kreft Distributing Co.
Box 105
Lake Havasu City, AZ 86403
(602) 855-2059
Product codes: **AHC   AHW   APO
CFL   CCM   COC   STL   SYL
KIT   CMP   CMG   CMA**

Matrix Inc.
537 S. 31st St.
Mesa, AZ 85204
(602) 832-1380
Product code: **INS**

Solar Energy Applications, Inc.
1102 E. Washington St.
Phoenix, AZ 85034
(602) 244-1822
Product codes: **AHW   APO   CFL
STL   SYL   KIT   LAB**

Solar Utility Systems
2430 S. 20th St.
Phoenix, AZ 85034
(602) 258-3671
Product codes: **AHW   AHE   APO
CFL**

Solar World, Inc.
4449 N. 12th St. (Suite 7)
Phoenix, AZ 85014
(602) 266-5686
Product codes: **CFL   STL   COS
SYL   AHW   AHE   APO**

SOLAREQUIP
P.O. Box 21447
Phoenix, AZ 85036
(602) 267-1166
Product codes: **AHE   AHW   APO
CFL   STL   SYL   CCM   CMM
CMP   KIT   COC**

Sunpower Systems Corp.
510 S. 52nd St. (Suite 101)
Tempe, AZ 85281
(602) 968-7425
Product codes: **AHW   AHC   APO
CCN   FEA   SYL**

Sunshine Unlimited
900 N. Jay St.
Chandler, AZ 85224
(602) 963-3878
Product codes: **AHW   AHE   CFL**

CALIFORNIA

Acurex Aerotherm
485 Clyde Ave.
Mountain View, CA 94042
(415) 964-3200
Product codes: **AHC   AHW   CCN
CMT   AAG   FEA**

Advanced Energy Technology
121 Albright
Los Gatos, CA 95030
(408) 866-7686
Product codes: **AHW   AHE   APO
CFL   SYL**

Advanced Solar Energy Systems, Inc.
3440 Wilshire Blvd.
Los Angeles, CA 90010
(213) 383-0035
Product codes: **AHC   AHW   APO
CFL**

Albatross Div./Dri-Honing Corp.
975 Terminal Way
San Carlos, CA 94070
(415) 593-1465
Product codes: **AHW   APO   CFL
SPC   KIT   ASH**

Alten Associates, Inc.
2594 Leghorn St.
Mountain View, CA 94043
(415) 969-6474
Product codes: **AHW   CFL   FEA
SYL   KIT   AHC   APO**

Altenergy
P.O. Box 695
Ben Lomond, CA 95005
(408) 336-2321
Product codes: **AHW   APO   AHE
AAG   CTU   CCN   CFL   COS
COC   HEX   RCE   LAB**

American Appliance Mfg. Corp.
P.O. Box 1956 (2341 Michigan Ave.)
Santa Monica, CA 90404
(213) 870-8541
Product codes: **AHW   CFL   STL
SYL**

American Solar
1749 Pine St.
Concord, CA 94522
(415) 798-9120
Product codes: **AHE   AHW   APO
CFL**

American Solar Mfg.
P.O. Box 194
Byron, CA 94514
(415) 634-2426
Product codes: AHW   APO   AHE
CFL   CCM   CMP   NBS

American Solar Systems
415 Branch St.
Arroyo Grande, CA 93420
(805) 481-1010
Product codes: AHW   AHC   APO
ACA   ACD   AGH   AMH   AAG
CFL   CTU   COS   SYL   LAB

American Sun Industries
3477 Old Conejo Rd. (P.O. Box 263)
Newbury Park, CA 91320
(805) 498-9700
Product codes: AHE   CFL   SYL
KIT   APO   FEA

Applied Sol Tech, Inc.
P.O. Box 9111 Cabrillo Station
Long Beach, CA 90810
(213) 426-0127
Product codes: AHC   CCN   CCM
COS   HEX   AHW   APO   STL
SYL   CMP   CMH

Aqueduct Inc.
1934 Cotner Ave.
Los Angeles, CA 90025
(213) 477-2496
Product codes: COS   COC

Astron Solar Industries, Inc.
465 McCormick St.
San Leandro, CA 94577
(415) 632-5400
Product codes: AHE   AHW   APO
CFL   COS   SYL   FEA

Aztec Solar Energy Systems of Orange City
420 Terminal St.
Santa Ana, CA 92701
(714) 558-0882
Product codes: APO   CFL

A-1 Prototype
1288 Fayette
El Cajon, CA 92020
(714) 449-6726
Product codes: AHE   AHW   APO
CFL   STL   SYL   KIT   FEA   NBS
ASH   COS

Baker Bros. Solar Collectors
207 Cortez Ave.
Davis, CA 95616
(916) 756-4558
Product codes: AHE   AHW   APO
SYL   CFL   KIT

Bostik-Finch, Inc.
20846 S. Normandie Ave.
Torrance, CA 90502
(213) 320-6800
Product codes: CCM   CMC

Bow Jon
2829 Burton Ave.
Burbank, CA 91504
(213) 846-2620
Product codes: AHW   CFL

Burke Industries, Inc.
2250 South 10th St.
San Jose, CA 95112
(408) 297-3500
Product codes: COS   COC   KIT
APO   CFL   FEA   SYL

California Solar Systems Co.
421 Picadilly (Suite 12)
San Bruno, CA 94066
(415) 583-4711
Product codes: AHW   CFL   SYL

J. W. Carroll & Sons
22600 S. Bonita St.
Carson, CA 90745
(213) 775-6737
Product codes: CCM   CMG

Castor Development Corp.
634 Crest Dr.
El Cajon, CA 92021
(714) 280-6660
Product codes: AHE   AHW   APO
AGH   AMH   CFL   CCM   CMA
COS   COC   STL   SYL   HEX
HEP   HEL   KIT   FEA   NBS   LAB

Catel Mfg. Inc.
235 W. Maple Ave.
Monrovia, CA 91016
(213) 359-2593
Product codes: APO   SPC

Colt Inc.
71590 San Jainto
Rancho Mirage, CA 92270
(714) 346-8033
Product codes: AHW   AHE   APO
CFL   CCM   CMH   COS   COC

(Products continued)

STL SYL INS HEX HEP KIT
LAB ASH

Conserdyne Corp.
4437 San Fernando Rd.
Glendale, CA 91204
(213) 246-8408
Product codes: **AHW   AHE   APO
CFL   SYL   HEX**

Cushing Instruments
7911 Hershel Ave.
La Jolla, CA 92037
(714) 459-3433
Product code: **INS**

Dearing Solar Energy Systems
12324 Ventura Blvd./P.O. Box 1744
Studio City, CA 91604
(213) 769-2521
Product codes: **APO   SPC   CFL**

Ecosol Ltd.
3382 El Camino Ave.
Sacramento, CA 95821
(916) 485-5860
Product codes: **AHC   AHW   COS
HEP   INS**

The Energy Factory
5622 E. Westover (Suite 105)
Fresno, CA 93727
(209) 292-6622
Product code: **AGH**

Energy Absorption Systems, Inc.
860 S. River Rd.
West Sacramento, CA 95691
(916) 371-3900
Product codes: **AHW   AHE   CFL
CCM   CMM   STL   SYL   HEX**

Energy Sealants, Inc.
1611 Borel Place (Suite 230)
San Mateo, CA 94402
(415) 574-0898
Product codes: **CCM   CMS**

Energy Systems, Inc.
4570 Alvarado Canyon Rd. (Bldg. D)
San Diego, CA 92120
(714) 280-6660
Product codes: **AHW   AHE   CFL
FEA   APO   COC   STL   CMP
CCM   CMG   CMA   CCN**

Era Del Sol
5960 Mandarin Ave.
Goleta, CA 93017
(805) 967-2116

Product codes: **AHE   AHW   APO
CFL   SYL   FEA**

Fafco
138 Jefferson Dr.
Menlo Park, CA 94025
(415) 321-6311
Product codes: **APO   CFL   FEA
COS   SYL   HEX**

Filon
12333 S. Van Ness Ave.
Hawthorne, CA 90250
(213) 757-5141
Product codes: **CCM   CMG**

Fred Rice Productions
P.O. Box 643 (48780 Eisenhower Dr.)
La Quinto, CA 92253
Product codes: **AHW   APO   CFL
STL   SYL   CFA   CTU   SYP
AHE   AMH**

Gamma Scientific, Inc.
3777 Ruffin Rd.
San Diego, CA 92123
(714) 279-8034
Product code: **INS**

Grundfos Pumps Corp.
2555 Clovis Ave.
Clovis, CA 93612
(209) 299-9741
Product codes: **CCM   CMP**

Hadbar/Div. of Purosil, Inc.
723 S. Fremont Ave.
Alhambra, CA 91803
(213) 283-0721
Product codes: **CCM   CMS**

Harness the Sun
P.O. Box 109
Cardiff-by-the-Sea, CA 92007
(714) 436-4822
Product codes: **APO   CFL   SYL
AHE   AHW**

Heliodyne Corp.
770 S. 16th
Richmond, CA 94804
(415) 237-9614
Product codes: **SYL   APO   AHW
AHE   CFL   KIT   CCM   CMH
COS   HEX**

Helios Solar Engineering
400 Warrington Ave.
Redwood City, CA 94063
(415) 369-6414
Product codes: **AHW   APO   CFL
COS   STL**

Heliotrope General
3733 Kenora Drive
Spring Valley, CA 92077
(714) 460-3930
Product codes: **AHC   AHW   APO
COC   STL   CCM   CMP   HEX**

Helio-Dynamics, Inc.
327 N. Fremont St.
Los Angeles, CA 90012
(213) 624-5888
Product codes: **AHC   AHW   APO
CFL   SYL   FEA**

Helix Solar Systems
P.O. Box 2038
La Puente, CA 91746
(213) 330-3312
Product codes: **AHW   APO   CFL
HEX   KIT   NBS**

Hexcel Corp.
11711 Dublin Blvd.
Dublin, CA 94566
(415) 828-4200
Product codes: **AHC   CCN   FEA**

Highland Mfg. Co.
P.O. Box 563
Yucaipa, CA 92399
Product codes: **APO   CFL**

Highland Plating Co.
1128 N. Highland Ave.
Los Angeles, CA 90038
(213) 469-2288
Product codes: **CCM   CMC**

HY-CAL Engineering
12105 Los Nietos Rd.
Santa Fe Springs, CA 90670
(213) 698-7785
Product code: **INS**

In Solar Systems
2562 W. Middlefield Rd.
Mountain View, CA 94043
(415) 964-2801
Product codes: **APO   CFL   HEX
KIT   LAB**

Jacobs-Del Solar Systems, Inc.
251 S. Lake Ave.
Pasadena, CA 91101
(213) 449-2171
Product codes: **CCN   AHC   AHW
APO   CCM   CMT   COC   SYL
FEA**

J. G. Johnston Co.
33458 Angeles Forest Hwy.
Palmdale, CA 93550
(805) 947-3791
Product codes: **AHE   CFA   FEA
AHW   SYA   STA**

Kahl Scientific Instruments Corp.
P.O. Box 1166
El Cajon, CA 92022
(714) 444-2158
Product code: **INS**

Kasaki USA
4150 Arch Dr. (Suite 8)
Studio City, CA 91604
(213) 985-9611
Product codes: **AHW   APO   CFL
COS   STL   SYL**

Wm. Lamb Co.
P.O. Box 4185
North Hollywood, CA 91607
(213) 764-6363
Product codes: **AHC   CCC   KIT**

MacBall Industries
3040 Market St.
Oakland, CA 94608
(415) 658-2228
Product code: **SPC**

Molectron Corp.
177 N. Wolfe Rd.
Sunnyvale, CA 94086
(408) 738-2661
Product code: **INS**

**Natural Energy Systems/
Marketing Arms Div.**
1632 Pioneer Way
El Cajon, CA 92020
(714) 440-6411
Product codes: **AHW   CFL   FEA
APO   AHC**

Natural Heating Systems
207 Cortez Ave.
Davis, CA 95616
(916) 756-4558
Product codes: **AHW   AHE   APO   CFL**

M. C. Nottingham Co.
4922 Irwindale Ave. (P.O. Box 2107)
Irwindale, CA 91706
(213) 283-0407
Product codes: **AHE   STL**

OCLI-Optical Coating Lab, Inc.
2789 Giffen Ave.

Santa Rosa, CA 95403
(707) 545-6440
Product codes: **CCM   CMG   CMA
CMC   CMR**

Coin Solar Systems
26010 Eden Landing Rd. (Suite 5)
Hayward, CA 94545
(415) 785-2000
Product codes: **CCM   CMA   CMP
INS**

Optical Sciences Group Inc.
24 Tiburon St.
San Rafael, CA 94901
(415) 453-8980
Product codes: **AHE   CCM   CMF**

Owen Enterprises
436 N. Fries Ave.
Wilmington, CA 90744
(213) 835-7436
Product codes: **AHC   CCN   APO**

Passive Solar Varient Homes by Savell
575 Birch Court (Suite A)
Colton, CA 92324
(714) 825-3394
Product codes: **AHC   SYP**

Piper Hydro, Inc.
2895 E. La Palma
Anaheim, CA 92806
(714) 630-4040
Product codes: **AHE   AHW   CFL
FEA   APO   SYL**

Powell Brothers, Inc.
5903 Firestone Blvd.
South Gate, CA 90280
(213) 869-3307
Product codes: **AHE   AHW   CFL
FEA   APO**

Raypak Inc.
31111 Agoura Rd.
Westlake Village, CA 91359
(213) 889-1500
Product codes: **AHE   AHW   APO
CFL   FEA   SYL   CCM   CMM
CMP   NBS**

Ra-Los Inc.
559 Union Ave.
Campbell, CA 95008
(408) 371-1734
Product codes: **INS   RCE   FEA
NBS   LAB   ASH   APO   AAG
CCM   CMG   CMH   CMI   CMM
CMP   AHC   AHW   CFL   SYL
STL   HEX   COS   COC**

Rho Sigma
11922 Valerio St.
North Hollywood, CA 91605
(213) 982-6800
Product codes: **AHW   AHE   APO
COS   COC   INS**

**Robert Shaw Controls Co./
Uni-Line Div.**
P.O. Box 2000 (4190 Temescal St.)
Corona, CA 91720
(714) 734-2600
Product codes: **AHC   AHW   APO
COC**

David Rose Steel Co.
345 N. Montgomery
San Jose, CA 95110
(408) 295-6975
Product codes: **AHE   AHW   STL**

Sealed Air Corp.
2015 Saybrook Ave.
Commerce, CA 90040
(213) 685-9666
Product codes: **APO   SPC**

**SETSCO (Solar Energy Thermal
Systems Co.)**
10378 Shary Circle
Concord, CA 94518
(415) 676-5392
Product codes: **AHE   AHW   APO
CFL**

Skytherm Processes Engineering
2424 Wilshire Blvd.
Los Angeles, CA 90057
(213) 389-2300
Product codes: **AHC   AHW   SYP
FEA**

A. O. Smith Corp.
P.O. Box 484
Newark, CA 94560
(415) 792-1345
Product codes: **AHE   AHW   STL
SYL**

Sol Power Industries, Inc.
10211-C Bubb Rd.
Cupertino, CA 95014
(408) 996-3222
Product codes: **AHE   AHW   APO
CFL   SYL**

Sol Ray
204 B Carleton
Orange, CA 92667
(714) 997-9431
Product codes: **AHW   AHE   APO**

AMH   AAG   CFA   CCM   CMG
CMA   CMI   CMS   CMM   CMR
CMP   CMB   COS   COC   STA
SYA   INS   HEX   LAB

Sola Heat
1200 E. 1st St.
Los Angeles, CA 90033
(213) 263-5823
Product codes: **AHE   AHW   CFL
STL   SYL**

Solar Applications, Inc.
7926 Convoy Court
San Diego, CA 92111
(714) 292-1857
Product codes: **AHE   AHW   APO
CFL   FEA   CCM   CMM   SPC
NBS**

Solar Captivators Systems, Inc.
7192 Clairemont Mesa Blvd.
San Diego, CA 92111
(714) 560-7454
Product codes: **AHW   APO   AHC
AAG   CFL**

Solar Collectors of Santa Cruz
2902 Glen Canyon Rd.
Santa Cruz, CA 95060
(408) 476-6369
Product codes: **AHW   AHE   APO
AHC   AGH   AMH   AAG   CFA
CFL   CCN   CCM   CMA   CMM
STA   STL   SYP   SYL   SYA   KIT
HEX**

Solar Concepts
12103 Washington Pl.
Los Angeles, CA 90066
(213) 398-5872
Product codes: **AHE   AHW   CFL**

Solar Concept, Inc.
818 Charcot Ave.
San Jose, CA 95131
(408) 263-8110
Product codes: **AHE   AHW   APO
AGH   AMH   AAG   CFL   ASH**

Solar Contact Systems
1415 Vernon
Anaheim, CA 92805
(714) 991-8120
Product codes: **AHW   CFL   STL
SYL   KIT**

Solar Energy Digest
P.O. Box 17776
San Diego, CA 92117
Product codes: **AHW   CFL   KIT**

Solar Energy Engineering
31 Maxwell Court
Santa Rosa, CA 95401
(707) 542-4498
Product codes: **AHW   AHE   APO
CFL**

Solar Energy, Inc.
12155 Magnolia Ave (6-E)
Riverside, CA 92503
(714) 785-0610
Product codes: **AHW   AHC   APO
CFL**

Solar Energy People
5044 Fair Grounds Dr.
Mariposa, CA 95338
(209) 966-5616
Product codes: **AHW   APO   CFL
CCM   CMA   COS   COC   STL
SYL   KIT**

Solar Energy Systems, Inc.
2345 Santa Fe Ave.
Los Angeles, CA 90058
(213) 472-6508
Product codes: **AHE   AHW   APO
CFL   COS   COC   SYL   CCM
CMA   CMM   KIT**

Solar Enterprises
9803 E. Rush St.
El Monte, CA 91733
(213) 444-2551
Product codes: **APO   CFL   FEA**

Solar Enterprises
P.O. Box 1046
Red Bluff, CA 96080
(916) 527-0551
Product codes: **AHE   AHW   APO
AMH   AAG   CFL   CCM   CMG
CMA   CMM   CMR   COS   COC
STL   SYL   INS   LAB**

Solar Equipment Corp.
P.O. Box 357
Lakeside, CA 92040
Product codes: **AHC   AHW   APO
CFL**

Solar Hydro Systems, Inc.
765 S. State College (Suite E)
Fullerton, CA 92631
(714) 992-4470
Product codes: **AHW   AHE   APO
AAG   CFL   COS   STL   SYL
SPC   INS**

Solar King International
8577 Canoga Ave.
Canoga Park, CA 91304

(213) 998-6400
Product codes: **AHE   AHW   CFL
SYL   COC   APO**

Solar Physics Corp.
1350 Hill St. (Suite A)
El Cajon, CA 92020
(714) 440-1625
Product codes: **AHC   CFL   CCN
FEA   AHW   APO**

Solar Pools, Inc.
2200 Freed Way
Pittsburg, CA 94565
(415) 432-7344
Product codes: **APO   CFL**

Solar Research Systems
3001 Red Hill Ave.
Costa Mesa, CA 92626
(714) 545-4941
Product codes: **APO   CFL   COS
SYL   FEA**

Solar Supply, Inc.
9163 Chesapeake Dr.
San Diego, CA 92123
(714) 292-7811
Product codes: **COS   COC   AHW**

Solar Systems
26046 Eden Landing Rd.
Hayward, CA 94545
(415) 785-0711
Product codes: **AHE   AHW   APO
CFA   CFL   CCM   COC   STL
STC   SYA   SYL   HEP   HEX   KIT
CMP   CMB**

Solar Tec Corp.
8250 Vickers St.
San Diego, CA 92111
(714) 560-8434
Product codes: **APO   AHC   AHW
CFL   FEA   CCN   SYL   HEP
NBS**

Solar Utilities
P.O. Box 1696 (2850 Mesa Verde Dr.)
Costa Mesa, CA 92626
(714) 557-7125
Product codes: **APO   CFL**

Solar West
2711 Chicago Ave.
Riverside, CA 92507
(714) 684-1555
Product codes: **APO   CFL**

Solar West, Inc.
3636 N. Hazel #108 (P.O. Box 892)
Fresno, CA 93714
(209) 222-3455
Product codes: **AHW   AHE   APO   CFL**

Solarbeam Industries, Inc.
118 N. Almansor St.
Alhambra, CA 91801
(213) 282-8451
Product codes: **AHE   AHW   CFL**

Solarcoa
21157 E. Spring St.
Long Beach, CA 90808
(213) 426-7655
Product codes: **AHE   AHW   CFL
FEA   SYL   APO   COC   CCM
CMP   CMM**

Solargenics Inc.
9713 Lurline Ave.
Chatsworth, CA 91311
(213) 998-0806
Product codes: **AHW   CFL   SYL
KIT   AHE   COS   CCM   CMM
CMP   HEX   STL   NBS   FEA**

Solarmaster
722-D W. Betteravia Rd.
Santa Maria, CA 93454
(805) 922-0205
Product codes: **CFL   CCN   KIT
AHC   AHW   APO   AGH   AAG**

The Solarshingles Co.
14532 Vanowen St.
Van Nuys, CA 91405
(213) 782-2828
Product codes: **AHE   AHW   APO
CFL   CFA**

Solarway
P.O. Box 217
Redwood Valley, CA 95470
(707) 485-7616
Product codes: **AHE   CCM   CMG**

SOLASTOR (Energy Absorption Syst.)
860 S. River Rd.
W. Sacramento, CA 95691
(916) 371-3900
Product codes: **AHW   AHC   APO
CFL   STL   SYL   HEX   CCM
CMP   CMM   COS   COC**

Solergy Inc.
70 Zoe St.
San Francisco, CA 94107
(415) 495-4303

Product codes: **AHE   AHW   CFL
CCN   NBS   FEA**

Southwest Air Conditioning Inc.
7268 El Cajon Blvd.
San Diego, CA 92115
(714) 462-0512
Product codes: **AHW   AHE   APO
AMH   CFL   STL**

Southwest Solar Corp.
8235 Remmet Ave.
Canoga Park, CA 91304
(213) 339-4383
Product codes: **AHW   CFL   COS
STL**

Spectran Instruments
P.O. Box 891
La Habra, CA 90631
(213) 694-3995
Product codes: **AHC   AHW   INS**

Spectrclab
12500 Gladstone Ave.
Sylmar, CA 91342
(213) 365-4611
Product code: **INS**

Sun of Man Solar Systems
Drawer W
Bethel Island, CA 94511
(415) 634-1223
Product codes: **AHW   APO   COC**

Sun Power Solar Engr. Co.
4032 Helix St.
Spring Valley, CA 92077
(714) 464-5322
Product codes: **AHE   AHW   CCN
CCM   CMT**

Sun Power Systems Ltd.
1024 W. Maude Ave. (Suite 203)
Sunnyvale, CA 94086
(408) 738-2442
Product codes: **AHE   AHW   KIT
CFL   SYL   APO**

Sun Water, Inc.
P.O. Box 732
Northridge, CA 91324
(213) 886-3620
Product codes: **AHW   APO   CCN**

Sunburst Solar Energy, Inc.
P.O. Box 2799
Menlo Park, CA 94025
(415) 327-8022
Product codes: **AHE   AHW   APO**

**CFL   FEA   COS   STL   HEX
KIT   CCM   CMG   CMP   NBS
ASH**

Sundu Co.
3319 Keys Lane
Anaheim, CA 92804
(714) 828-2873
Product codes: **APO   CFL   FEA
AHE   AHW**

Sunglaze
P.O. Box 2634
Olympic Valley, CA 95730
(702) 831-2400
Product codes: **AHW   AHE   AAG
AGH   CFA   SYA**

Sunrise Solar, Inc.
7359 Reseda Blvd.
Reseda, CA 91335
(213) 881-3164
Product codes: **AHE   AHW   CFL**

Sunshine Greenhouses
109 Cooper St. (Suite 5)
Santa Cruz, CA 95060
(408) 425-1451
Product codes: **AGH   AHW   APO
CFL**

Sunshine Utility Co.
1444 Pioneer Way (Suite 9 & 10)
El Cajon, CA 92020
(714) 440-3151
Product codes: **AHE   AHW   CFL
APO   FEA**

Sunspot Environmental Energy Systems
P.O. Box 5110
San Diego, CA 92105
(714) 264-9100
Product codes: **AHW   AHE   APO
CFL   SYL   KIT**

Sunspot (Div. Elcam, Inc.)
5330 Debbie Lane
Santa Barbara, CA 93111
(805) 964-8676
Product codes: **AHE   CFA   FEA
CCM   SYL   CFL   COC   AHW
STL   CMP**

Sunstream Environments
P.O. Box 93A (Los Osos Valley Rd.)
San Luis Obispo, CA 93401
(805) 541-0760
Product codes: **AAG   AGH   CFA**

Sunwater Energy Products
1488 Pioneer Way (Suite 17)
El Cajon, CA 92020
(714) 579-0771
Product codes: **AHW   APO   CFL
COS   AGH   AHE   CCM   CMA**

Sunworks
1501 Felta Rd.
Healdsburg, CA 95448
(707) 433-3693
Product codes: **AHE   AHW   APO
CFL**

Swan Solar
6909 Eton St. (Unit G)
Canoga Park, CA 91303
(213) 884-7874
Product codes: **AHW   AHE   APO
CFL   HEX**

Swedlow Inc.
12122 Western Ave.
Garden Grove, CA 92645
(714) 893-7531
Product codes: **CCM   CMF**

Technical Measurements, Inc.
P.O. Box 838
La Canada, CA 91011
(213) 248-1035
Product code: **INS**

Technitrek Corp.
1999 Pike Ave.
San Leandro, CA 94577
(415) 352-0535
Product codes: **AHW   APO   CFL
CCM   CMP   COS   COC   AHE
STL   SYL**

Troger Enterprises
2024 "A" De La Vina
Santa Barbara, CA 93105
(805) 687-6522
Product codes: **AHE   AHW   APO
COS**

Unitspan Architectural Systems, Inc.
9419 Mason Ave.
Chatsworth, CA 91311
(213) 998-1131
Product codes: **AHE   AHW   CFL
APO   KIT   FEA**

Vanguard Energy Systems
9133 Chesapeake Dr.
San Diego, CA 92123
(714) 292-1433
Product codes: **CCM   CMP   COS   HEP**

Vanguard Solar Systems
2727 Coronado St.
Anaheim, CA 92806
(714) 871-8181
Product codes: **AHW   APO   CFL**

Vinyl-Fab Industries
10800 St. Louis Dr.
El Monte, CA 91731
Product code: **SPC**

Weathermeasure Corp.
P.O. Box 41257
Sacramento, CA 95841
(916) 481-7565
Product code: **INS**

Weathertronics
2777 Del Monte St.
West Sacramento, CA 95691
(916) 371-2660
Product code: **INS**

Western Energy, Inc.
454 Forest Ave.
Palo Alto, CA 94302
(415) 327-3371
Product codes: **AHE   AHW   APO
CFL   COC   STL   HEX   CMP
CCM   NBS**

Western Solar Development, Inc.
1236 Callen St.
Vacaville, CA 95688
(707) 446-4411
Product codes: **AHC   AHW   APO
CFL   KIT**

Wojick Industries, Inc.
527 N. Main St.
Fallbrook, CA 92028
(714) 728-5593
Product codes: **APO   CFL   SYL
COC**

Ying Mfg. Corp.
1957 W. 144th St.
Gardena, CA 90249
(213) 327-8399
Product codes: **AHW   CFL   FEA
AHC   APO   SYL   CFA   HEX
KIT   CCM   CMP   CMB   CMM
NBS   ASH   STL   STA**

ZZ Corp.
10806 Kaylor St.
Los Alamitos, CA 90720
(213) 598-3220
Product codes: **AHW   AHE   AGH
AMH   CCN   CCM   CMI   CMM**

CMT CMR COC STL SYL
INS FEA NBS LAB ASH

COLORADO
American Helio Thermal Corp.
(Miromit)
2625 S. Santa Fe Dr.
Denver, CO 80223
(303) 778-0650
Product codes: AHW   CFL   FEA
APO   SYL   AHC

Barber-Nichols Engrg.
6325 W. 55th Ave.
Arvada, CO 80002
(303) 421-8111
Product codes: ACO   RCE

Colorado Sunworks Corp.
P.O. Box 455
Boulder, CO 80306
(303) 443-9199
Product codes: AHW   AHE   AGH
AAG   CFL   COS   COC   STL
SYL   HEX   KIT   NBS   LAB   ASH
SYP   CFA   CCM   CMB

Design Works
Box 700
Telluride, CO 81435
Product codes: AHW   CFA   AHE
COC   KIT

Energy Dynamics Corp.
327 West Vermijo Road
Colorado Springs, CO 80903
(303) 475-0332
Product codes: AHW   CFL   FEA
APO   CCM   COS   COC   STL
STC   SYL   HEP   AHC

Entropy Ltd.
5735 Arapahoe Ave.
Boulder, CO 80303
(303) 443-5103
Product codes: AHW   AHC   SYL
STL   AAG   CCN

Federal Energy Corp.
5505 E. Evans
Denver, CO 80222
(303) 753-0565
Product codes: AHE   AHW   CFL
COC   HEX   AHC   ACA   CCN
STL   SYL   CCM   CMP

First International Corp.
1354 Ford St.
Colorado Springs, CO 80915
(303) 574-4404

Product codes: AHE   AHW   CFA
SYA   STA   COS

Future Systems, Inc.
12500 W. Cedar Dr.
Lakewood, CO 80228
(303) 989-0431
Product codes: AHE   APO   CFA
SSF

General Solar Corp.
5575 S. Sycamore St.
Littleton, CO 80120
(303) 321-2675
Product codes: AHW   AHE   SYL
HEP   HEX

International Solar Industries, Inc.
9555 E. Caley
Englewood, CO 80110
Product codes: AHE   AHW   CFA
SYL

International Solarthermics Corp.
P.O. Box 397
Nederland, CO 80466
(303) 258-3272
Product codes: AHE   SSF

R. M. Products
5010 Cook St.
Denver, CO 80216
(303) 825-0203
Product codes: AHE   AHW   CFL
CFA   SYA   FEA   CCM   CMM
APO   AGH   COS   COC   STA
STL   SYL   SYP

Solar Control Corp.
5595 Arapahoe
Boulder, CO 80302
(303) 449-9180
Product codes: AHE   COC   COS

Solar Dynamics, Inc.
1320 S. Lipan St.
Denver, CO 80223
(303) 777-3666
Product codes: AHE   SSF

Solar Energy Research Corp.
701B S. Main St.
Longmont, CO 80501
(303) 772-8406
Product codes: AHC   AHW   APO
HEP   CCM   CMM   CMP   STL
KIT   COS   COC   CMA   CMT
INS   HEX   NBS

Solar Power West
709 Spruce St.
Aspen, CO 81611
(303) 925-4698
Product codes: APO   CFL   KIT

Solar Seven Industries, Inc.
3323 Moline St.
Aurora, CO 80110
(303) 364-7277
Product codes: AHE   AHW   APO
CFA   SYA   NBS

Solar Technology Corp.
2160 Clay
Denver, CO 80211
Product codes: CFA   SYA   AHC
KIT   FEA   AGH   SSF

Solaron Corp.
300 Galleria Tower
720 S. Colorado
Denver, CO 80222
(303) 759-0101
Product codes: AHE   CFA   FEA
AHW   CCM   COS   STA   SYA
HEX   CMP   NBS

Sol-Aire
Energy Systems Inc.
2750 S. Shoshone
Englewood, CO 80110
(303) 761-4335
Product codes: APO   AHC   AHW
SYA   CFA   STA   NBS   LAB   ASH

Sun Power of Colorado
343 Van Gordan St.
Bldg. 18/406
Lakewood, CO 80228
(303) 988-6200
Product codes: AHC   AHW   CFA

Sun-Heet, Inc.
2624 South Zuni
Englewood, CO 80110
(303) 922-6179
Product codes: AHW   APO   AHC
AGH   AAG   CCN   STL   SYL

Tri-State Sol-Aire, Inc.
7100 Broadway (Suite 6N)
Denver, CO 80221
(303) 426-4000
Product codes: AHW   AHE   CFA
COS   STA   SYA   HEP

The Tub Co.
Box 8
Boulder, CO 80306

(303) 449-4563
Product codes: AHE   AHW   SYL
KIT

CONNECTICUT

American Solar Heat Corp.
7 National Pl.
Danbury, CT 06810
(203) 792-0077
Product codes: AHW   AHE   COC
SYL   CFL   INS

Barnes Engrg. Co.
30 Commerce Rd.
Stamford, CT 06904
(203) 348-5381
Product code: INS

C & M Systems, Inc.
P.O. Box 475 (Saybrook Ind. Park)
Old Saybrook, CT 06475
(203) 388-3429
Product code: COC

Enthone Inc.
Sunworks Div.
P.O. Box 1004
New Haven, CT 06508
(203) 934-6301
Product codes: AHW   CFA   CFL
FEA   CCM   SYA   SYL   CMH
AHE   KIT

Falbel Energy Systems Corp.
P.O. Box 6
Greenwich, CT 06830
(203) 357-0626
Product codes: CCN   FEA   AHW
APO   KIT   COS   CCM   CMA
CFL   STL   SYL   HEX   AHE
CMP   CMG   CMH   CMI

FTA Corp.
348 Hazard Ave.
Enfield, CT 06082
(203) 749-7054
Product codes: AHW   AHE   CFA
COS

Groundstar Energy Corp.
137 Rowayton Ave.
Rowayton, CT 06853
(203) 838-0650
Product codes: AHW   COS   APO
AHC   CFL   SYL   CCM   CMM
NBS   ASH

International Environment Corp.
83 S. Water St.
Greenwich, CT 06830

(203) 531-4490
Product codes: **AHW   CFL   FEA
AHE   SYL**

**International Environmental
Energy, Inc.**
275 Windsor St.
Hartford, CT 06120
Product codes: **AHE   AHW   COS
COC   SYA   SYL**

Kem Associates
153 East St.
New Haven, CT 06507
(203) 865-0584
Product codes: **CCM   CMM**

National Solar Corp.
Novelty Lane
Essex, CT 06426
(203) 767-1644
Product codes: **AHW   CFL   CCM
CMM   KIT**

Nuclear Technology Corp.
P.O. Box 1
Amston, CT 06231
(203) 537-2387
Product codes: **AHE   AHW   CCM
CMH   CMI**

Oriel Corp. of America
15 Market St.
Stamford, CT 06902
(203) 357-1600
Product codes: **INS   LAB**

Research Technology Corp.
151 John Downey Dr.
New Britain, CT 06051
(203) 224-8155
Product codes: **CCM   CMH   INS
HEX**

Resource Technology
151 John Downey Dr.
New Britain, CT 06051
(203) 224-8155
Product codes: **AHC   AHW   CCM
CMH**

STA Corp.
P.O. Box 2284
348 Hazard Ave
Enfield, CT 06082
(203) 749-7054
Product codes: **AHE   AHW   CFA
CFL**

Solar Kinetics Corp.
P.O. Box 17308
West Hartford, CT 06117
(203) 233-4461
Product codes: **AHW   APO   AGH
AAG   CCN   CCM   COS   COC
STL   SYL   HEX   FEA   LAB   ASH**

Solar Products Mfg. Corp.
151 John Downey Dr.
New Britain, CT 06051
(203) 224-2164
Product codes: **AHE   AHW   APO
CFL   CCM   CMG   CMP   COS
SYL   HEX   KIT   FEA   NBS**

Spiral Tubing Corp.
533 John Downey Dr.
New Britain, CT 06051
(203) 244-2409
Product codes: **AHE   AHW   CCM
CMA**

Suntap Inc./Bross Utilities Svc. Inc.
42 East Dudley Town Rd.
Bloomfield, CT 06002
(203) 243-1781
Product codes: **AHW   AHC   APO
AGH   AMH   AAG   CFL   CTU
CCM   CMH   CMI   COS   COC
STL   SYL   INS   HEX   FEA   NBS
LAB   ASH**

Sunworks Div., Enthone Inc.
Box 1004
New Haven, CT 06508
(203) 934-6301
Product codes: **AHE   AHW   CFA
CFL   FEA   CCM   CMH   SYA
SYL   KIT**

Sun-Ray Solar Equipment
2093 Boston Ave.
Bridgeport, CT 06610
(203) 333-6264
Product codes: **AHE   AHW   APO
CFL**

Wilson Solar Kinetics Corp.
P.O. Box 17308
West Hartford, CT 06117
(203) 233-4461
Product codes: **CCN   FEA   AHW
APO   COS   CMP   STL   SYL
AAG   CCM   CMM**

Wormser Scientific Corp.
88 Foxwood Rd.
Stamford, CT 06903
(203) 322-1981
Product codes: **AHC   CCN**

DELAWARE

DuPont Co.
Nemours Bldg. (Rm. 24751)
Wilmington, DE 19898
(302) 999-3456
Product codes: AHW   AHE   CCM
CMG   CMH

Hercules Inc.
910 Market St.
Wilmington, DE 19899
Product codes: CCM   SYP   CMG
AGH

DISTRICT OF COLUMBIA

Natural Energy Corp.
1001 Connecticut Ave. N.W.
Washington, DC 20036
(202) 296-7070
Product codes: AHW   AHC   APO
CFL   AAG

Solartherm
1640 Kalmia Rd. N.W.
Washington, DC 20112
Product codes: AHW   AHC   CCN

Thomason Solar Homes, Inc.
6802 Walker Mill Rd. S.E.
Washington, DC 20027
(301) 292-5122
Product codes: AHW   CFL   CCM
COC   STL   SYL   AHC

FLORIDA

All Sunpower, Inc.
10400 S.W. 187th St.
Miami, FL 33157
(305) 233-2224
Product codes: AHC   AMH   CCM
CMG   AHW   APO   CFL   SYL
KIT   COS   COC   STL   SPC   INS
HEX   KIT   FEA   NBS   LAB
ASH

American Solar Power, Inc.
715 Swann Ave.
Tampa, FL 33606
(813) 251-6946
Product codes: AHW   CFL   FEA

Aqua Solar, Inc.
1234 Zacchini Ave.
Sarasota, FL 33577
(813) 366-7080
Product codes: APO   CTU   COS
COC   SYA   SPC   KIT   FEA   ASH

Astro Solar Corp.
457 Santa Anna Dr.
Palm Springs, FL 33460
(305) 965-0606
Product codes: AHW   AHC   ACA
AMH   AAG   CFL   CFA   CTU
CFE   COC   HEX   FEA   NBS   LAB

Aztec Solar Co.
2301 Dyan Way
Altamonte Springs, FL 32751
(305) 830-5477
Product codes: AHW   CFL   CCM
COC   SYL   COS   CMM   CMP

Beutels Solar Heating Co.
7161 N.W. 74th St.
Miami, FL 33166
(305) 885-0122
Product codes: AHW   CFL   FEA

D. W. Browning Contracting Co.
475 Carswell Ave.
Holly Hill, FL 32017
(904) 252-1528
Product codes: AHE   AHW   CFL
FEA   APO   SYL

Capital Solar Heating, Inc.
376 N.W. 25th St.
Miami, FL 33127
(305) 576-2380
Product codes: AHW   APO   AHC
CFL   STL   SYL   KIT   FEA

Chemical Processors, Inc.
P.O. Box 10636
St. Petersburg, FL 33733
(813) 822-3689
Product codes: AHE   AHW   CFL
FEA   SYL

Consumer Energy Corp.
4234 S.W. 75th Ave.
Miami, FL 33155
(305) 266-0124
Product codes: AHW   CFL   FEA
APO   STL

CSI Solar Systems Div.
12400 49th St.
Clearwater, FL 33520
(813) 577-4228
Product codes: AHE   AHW   CFL
FEA   APO   COS   STL   SYL

C.B.M. Manufacturing, Inc.
621 N.W. 6th Ave.
Fort Lauderdale, FL 33311
(305) 463-5810

Product codes: **AHW   CFL   COS
COC   STL   SYL   HEX   FEA
NBS   LAB**

Deko-Labs
3860 S.W. Archer Rd.
Gainesville, FL 32604
(904) 372-6009
Product code: **COC**

Energy Conservation Equipment Corp.
1011 South 6th Ave.
Lakeworth, FL 33460
(305) 586-3839
Product codes: **AHW   APO   AHC
CFL   COS   HEX   HEP   NBS
ASH**

Flagala Corp.
9700 W. Highway 98
Panama City, FL 32401
(904) 234-6559
Product codes: **AHE   AHW   CFL
FEA   APO   COS   STL**

Florida Solar Power, Inc.
P.O. Box 5846
Tallahassee, FL 32301
(904) 224-8270
Product codes: **AHE   AHW   CFL
FEA   COC   STL   STC   HEX
APO   CCM   COS   SYL   CMP
CMA   CMG**

General Energy Devices
1753 Ensley
Clearwater, FL 33516
(813) 586-3585
Product codes: **AHE   AHW   CFL
FEA   APO   CCM   COS   COC
STL   SYL   CMP   HEX   CMH
NBS   ASH**

Gulf Thermal Corp.
P.O. Box 13124
Airgate Branch
Sarasota, FL 33578
(813) 355-9783
Product codes: **AHE   AHW   CFL
FEA   APO   SYL**

Hawthorne Industries, Inc.
1501 S. Dixie
West Palm Beach, FL 33401
(305) 659-5400
Product code: **COS**

Hill Bros. Inc.
Thermill Div.
3501 N.W. 60th St.

Miami, FL 33142
Product codes: **AHW   AHE   APO
CFL   CCM   COS   STL   SYL
CMP   CMM**

Horizon Enterprises, Inc.
P.O. Box V
Homestead, FL 33030
(305) 245-5145
Product codes: **AHE   AHW   APO
AMH   CFL   NBS**

Largo Solar Systems, Inc.
991 S.W. 40th Ave.
Plantation, FL 33317
(305) 583-8090
Product codes: **AHW   CFL   FEA
APO   CCM   SYL   KIT   COS
CMP   CMA**

National Solar Systems
P.O. Box 82177
Tampa, FL 33682
(813) 935-9634
Product codes: **AHW   AHE   APO
CFL   COS   COC   STL   SYL
HEP   KIT   FEA   NBS**

OEM Products, Inc.
Solarmatic
2701 Adamo Dr.
Tampa, FL 33605
(813) 247-5947
Product codes: **AHW   APO   CFL
COC   AHC   FEA   CMM   CMP
HEP   CCM   CMH   STC   STP
STL   SYL   HEX**

W. R. Robbins & Son
1401 N.W. 20th St.
Miami, FL 33142
(305) 325-0880
Product codes: **AHW   CFL   FEA
APO   SYL   COS   COC   KIT
CCM   CMP   CMH   STL**

Rox International
2604 Hidden Lake Dr. (Suite D)
Sarasota, FL 33577
(813) 366-6053
Product codes: **AHW   AHE   CCN
RCE   LAB**

Semco Solar Products Corp.
5701 N.E. 14th Ave.
Ft. Lauderdale, FL 3334
(305) 565-2516
Product codes: **AHE   AHW   CFL
FEA   APO   SYL   STL   COC
CCM   CMP**

J & R Simmons Construction Co.
2185 Sherwood Dr.
South Daytona, FL 32019
(904) 677-5832
Product codes: AHE   AHW   CFL
SYL   FEA

Solar Controlar, Inc.
P.O. Box 8703
Orlando, FL 32806
Product codes: AHE   COS   AHW

Solar Development, Inc.
3630 Reese Ave.
Garden Ind. Park
Riviera Beach, FL 33404
(305) 842-8935
Product codes: AHE   AHW   CFA
CFL   FEA   APO   CCM   COC
SYL   CMM   CMA   CMP   NBS

Solar Dynamics, Inc.
P.O. Box 3457
Hialeah, FL 33013
(305) 921-7911
Product codes: AHE   AHW   CFL
FEA   SYL

Solar Electric International
2634 Taft Ave.
Orlando, FL 32804
(305) 422-8396
Product codes: AHC   AHW   CTU
SYL

Solar Energy Components, Inc.
1605 North Cocoa Blvd.
Cocoa, FL 32922
(305) 632-2880
Product codes: AHE   AHW   CFL
FEA   CCM   CMP   CMG   KIT
COC

Solar Energy Contractors
P.O. Box 17094
Jacksonville, FL 32216
(904) 641-5611
Product codes: AHE   AHW   CFL
FEA   COS   COC   STL   KIT
CCM   CMP   CMM

Solar Energy Products, Inc.
1208 N.W. 8th Ave.
Gainesville, FL 32601
(904) 377-6527
Product codes: AHE   AHW   APO
CFL   STL   SYL   KIT   HEX   COC
CCM   CMM   CMP   CMG   NBS

Solar Energy Resources Corp.
10639 S.W. 185 Terrace
Miami, FL 33157
(305) 233-0711
Product codes: AHW   CFL   FEA
AHC   APO   SYL   HEP   ACA

Solar Engrg. & Mfg. Co., Inc.
P.O. Box 1358
Boca Raton, FL 33432
(305) 368-2456
Product codes: INS   HEL   KIT
FEA   NBS   LAB   ASH   AHW
APO   CFL   CCN   CCM   CMG
CMA   CCM   CMT   CMR   COS
COC   STL   SYL

Solar Fin Systems
140 S. Dixie Highway
St. Augustine, FL 32084
(904) 824-3522
Product codes: AHW   AHE   CFL
COS   SYL

Solar Heater Mfg.
1011 6 Ave. South
Lake Worth, FL 33460
(305) 586-3839
Product codes: AHW   APO   AHC
CFL   ASH   AGH   AMH   COS
STL   SYL   INS   HEX   KIT   NBS
LAB

Solar Heating Systems
13584 49th St. North
Clearwater, FL 33520
(813) 577-3961
Product codes: AHE   AHW   CFL
FEA   APO   COS   COC   KIT   CCM

Solar Industries of Florida
P.O. Box 9013
Jacksonville, FL 32208
(904) 768-4323
Product codes: AHE   AHW   CFL
FEA

Solar Innovations
412 Longfellow Blvd.
Lakeland, FL 33801
(813) 688-8373
Product codes: AHW   SYL   AHE
APO   CFL   COS   INS   KIT   FEA
STL   CCM   CMM   CMP

Solar Pool Heaters of S.W. Florida
901 S.E. 13th Place
Cape Coral, FL 33904
(813) 542-1500
Product codes: APO   CFL   FEA

Solar Products, Inc./Sun-Tank
614 N.W. 62nd St.
Miami, FL 33150
(305) 756-7609
Product codes: **AHE   AHW   CFL
FEA   APO   KIT   COC   CCM
CMP**

Solar Systems by Sundance
4815 S.W. 75th Ave.
Miami, FL 33155
(305) 264-1894
Product codes: **AHE   AHW   CFL
FEA**

Solar Water Heaters of New Port Richey
1214 U.S. Highway 19 N.
New Port Richey, FL 33552
(813) 848-2343
Product codes: **AHW   AHE   APO
AMH   CFA   CCM   CMG   CMA
CMH   CMS   CMM   CMT   CMC
CMR   COS   STL   SYL   KIT   FEA
NBS   LAB   ASH**

Solarcell Corp.
1455 N.E. 57th St.
Fort Lauderdale, FL 33334
(305) 462-2215
Product codes: **AHW   APO   CCN
COS   CCM   CMM   KIT**

Solarkit of Florida, Inc.
1102 139th Ave.
Tampa, FL 33612
(813) 971-3934
Product codes: **AHE   AHW   CFL
KIT**

Solar-Eye Products, Inc.
1300 N.W. McNab (Bldgs. G & H)
Fort Lauderdale, FL 33309
(305) 974-2500
Product codes: **APO   AHW   AHE
CFL   SYL   COC   FEA**

Southern Lighting/
Universal 100 Products
501 Elwell Ave.
Orlando, FL 32803
(305) 894-8851
Product codes: **AHE   AHW   CFL
FEA   COS   CCM   CMM**

Sun Harvesters, Inc.
211 N.E. 5th St.
Ocala, FL 32670
(904) 629-0687
Product codes: **AHW   APO   AMH
AAG   STL   SYL   KIT**

Sun-Dance, Inc.
13939 N.W. 60th Ave.
Miami Lakes, FL 33014
(305) 557-2882
Product codes: **AHE   AHW   APO
CCM   CMP   STL   SYL**

Systems Technology, Inc.
P.O. Box 337
Shalimar, FL 32579
(904) 863-9213
Product codes: **AHW   APO   CFL
CCM   SYL   CMP   STL   HEX
COS   COC   FEA**

S.P.S. Inc.
8801 Biscayne Blvd.
Miami, FL 33138
(305) 754-7766
Product codes: **AHC   CCN   CTU
CCM   CMT   RCE**

Technology Applications Lab
1670 Highway A1A
Satellite Beach, FL 32937
(305) 777-1400
Product code: **INS**

Unit Electric Control, Inc./Sol-Ray Div.
130 Atlantic Dr.
Maitland, FL 32751
(305) 831-1900
Product codes: **AHE   AHW   CFL
FEA   COC   CCM   CMP   KIT**

Universal Solar Energy Co.
1802 Madrid Ave.
Lake Worth, FL 33461
(305) 586-6020
Product codes: **AHE   AHW   CFL
FEA   APO   CCM   COC   SYL
CMP**

Universal 100 Products/
Southern Lighting
501 Elwell Ave.
Orlando, FL 32803
(305) 894-8851
Product codes: **AHE   AHW   CFL**

Walker & Mart Solar Lab, Inc.
3584 Progress Ave.
Naples, FL 33942
(813) 262-6257
Product codes: **AHE   AHW   APO
AGH   CFL   STL   SYL   NBS**

Wilcon Corp.
3310 S.W. Seventh
Ocala, FL 32670

(904) 732-2550
Product codes: AHE   AHW   FEA
CFL   SYL   APO   COC   COS

Wilcox Mfg. Corp.
P.O. Box 455
Pinellas Park, FL 33565
(813) 531-7741
Product codes: AHW   AHE   APO
CFL   FEA   HEX   HEP

GEORGIA

Independent Living, Inc.
2300 Peachford Rd.
Doraville, GA 30340
(404) 455-0927
Product codes: AHC   AHW   APO
COC   COS   SYL

National Solar Co.
2331 Adams Dr. N.W.
Atlanta, GA 30318
(404) 352-3478
Product codes: AHE   AHW   CFL
FEA   SYL

National Solar Sales, Inc.
165 W. Wieuca Rd. (Suite 100)
Atlanta, GA 30342
(404) 256-1660
Product codes: AHW   AHC   APO
CFL   STL   SYL

Scientific-Atlanta, Inc.
3845 Pleasantdale Rd.
Atlanta, GA 30340
(404) 449-2000
Product codes: AHE   AHW   CFL
FEA

Solar Energy Systems of Georgia
5825 Glenridge Dr. N.E. (Bldg. 2)
Atlanta, GA 30328
(404) 255-9588
Product codes: AHW   COS   COC
SYL   CFL   SYA   STL   CCM
CMP   HEX   AHE   ACA   AGH
AMH   CFA   SYP   HYB   INS   KIT

Solar Technology, Inc.
3927 Oakclif Industrial Ct.
Atlanta, GA 30340
(404) 449-0900
Product codes: AHE   AHW   CFL
CCM   COC   COS   STL   SYL
CMP   FEA

Southeastern Solar Systems, Inc.
2812 New Spring Rd. (Suite 150)
Atlanta, GA 30339

(404) 434-4447
Product codes: AHW   AHC   APO
CFL   FEA   CTU   CCN   CCM
STC   SYL   COS   STL   SYP   HEX
HEP   CMA   CMP   NBS   AAG

Southern Aluminum Finishing Co.
1581 Huber St. N.W.
Atlantic, GA 30318
(404) 355-1560
Product codes: CCM   CMC

Wallace Co.
831 Dorsey St.
Gainsville, GA 30501
(404) 534-5971
Product codes: AHE   AHW   CFL
FEA   CCM   SYL   APO   HEP

HAWAII

Solar Enterprises Hawaii
P.O. Box 27031
Honolulu, HI 96827
(808) 922-8528
Product codes: AHW   CFL   KIT

Solaray Corp.
2414 Makiki Heights Dr.
Honolulu, HI 96822
(808) 533-6464
Product codes: AHW   APO   CFL
SYL   AHE   FEA

IDAHO

Energy Alternatives, Inc.
1006 E "D" St.
Moscow, ID 83843
(208) 882-0200
Product codes: AHE   CFA   COS
STA   SYA   KIT

ILLINOIS

Airtex Corp.
2900 N. Western Ave.
Chicago, IL 60618
(312) 463-2500
Product codes: AHW   APO   AHC
ACA   AGH   AMH   CFL   CFE
CCM   CMG   CMA   CMM   CMC
CMP   COS   COC   STL   SYL
INS   HEX   FEA   NBS   ASH

Airtrol Corp.
203 W. Hawick St.
Rockton, IL 61072
(815) 624-8051
Product codes: AHE   CCM   CMB

American Chemet Corp.
P.O. Box 165
Deerfield, IL 60015
(312) 948-0800
Product codes: **AHE   CCM   CMC**

Chamberlain Mfg. Corp.
845 Larch Ave.
Elmhurst, IL 60126
(312) 279-3600
Product codes: **AHE   AHW   CFL
FEA**

Chicago Solar Corp.
1773 California St.
Rolling Meadows, IL 60008
(312) 358-1918
Product codes: **AHW   CFA**

DeSoto Inc.
1700 S. Mt. Prospect Rd.
Des Plaines, IL 60018
(312) 391-9434
Product codes: **CCM   CMC**

The Dexter Corp. (Midland Div.)
East Water St.
Waukegan, IL 60085
(312) 623-4200
Product codes: **CCM   CMC**

Heliodyne Inc.
4571 Linview Dr.
Rockford, IL 61109
(815) 874-6841
Product codes: **AHC   CFA   CCM
CMA   CMM   COS   STA   SYA**

Illinois Solar Corp.
P.O. Box 841
Peoria, IL 61652
(309) 673-0458
Product codes: **AHW   AHE   AAG
AMH   AGH   CFA   SYA   NBS
FEA   COS   STA   SYP   KIT**

ITT/Fluid Handling Div.
4711 Golf Rd.
Skokie, IL 60076
(312) 677-4030
Product codes: **AHC   AHW   CCM
CMP   HEX   COC**

Johnson Controls Inc./Penn. Div.
2221 Camden Ct.
Oak Brook, IL 60521
(312) 654-4900
Product codes: **AHE   AHW   APO
COS   COC**

March Mfg. Co., Inc.
1819 Pickwick Ave.
Glenview, IL 60025
(312) 729-5300
Product codes: **CCM   CMP**

National Industrial Sales
6501 W. 99th St.
Chicago Ridge, IL 60415
(312) 423-4924
Product codes: **AHE   AHW   CCM
CMG**

Natural Energy Systems, Inc.
1117 E. Carpenter Dr.
Palatine, IL 60067
(312) 359-6760
Product codes: **AHW   AHC   APO
CFL   COS   STL   HEX   HEP
SYL**

Olin Brass Corp./Roll-Bond Div.
E. Alton, IL 62024
(618) 258-2000
Product codes: **AHW   CCM   AHC
CMA**

Pak-Tronics Inc.
4044 N. Rockwell Ave.
Chicago, IL 60618
(213) 478-8585
Product codes: **AHE   AHW   COS
COC**

**Rheem Water Heater Div./
City Investing**
7600 Kedzie Ave.
Chicago, IL 60652
(312) 434-7500
Product codes: **AHW   STL**

S. S. Solar, Inc.
16 Keystone Ave.
River Forest, IL 60305
(312) 771-1912
Product codes: **AHW   AHC   CCN   SYL**

Shelley Radiant Ceiling Co.
8110 N. St. Louis Ave.
Skokie, IL 60076
Product codes: **APO   CCM**

A. O. Smith Corp.
Box 28
Kankakee, IL 60901
Product codes: **AHW   STL   STC**

Solar Dynamics Corp.
550 Frontage Rd.
Northfield, IL 60093
(312) 446-5242

Product codes: **AHW   CFL   SYL
AHE**

Sun Systems Inc.
P.O. Box 155
Eureka, IL 61530
(309) 467-3632
Product codes: **AHW   CFA   COS
APO   STL   SYA   FEA   AHC
AAG   SSF**

INDIANA

Arkla Industries, Inc.
P.O. Box 534
Evansville, IN 47704
(812) 424-3331
Product codes: **ACO   ACA**

A/C Fabricating Corp.
P.O. Box 774/64600 U.S. 33 East
Goshen, IN 46525
(219) 534-1415
Product code: **CCM**

C. F. Roark Welding & Enrg. Co., Inc.
136 N. Green St.
Brownsburg, IN 46112
(317) 852-3163
Product codes: **CFL   CCN   AHE
KIT**

IOWA

Decker Mfg./Impac Corp. Div.
312 Blondeau
Keokuk, IA 52632
(319) 524-3304
Product codes: **AHE   CFA   KIT
SYA**

Energy King
Box 248
Creston, IA 50801
(515) 782-8566
Product codes: **AHE   CFA**

Impac Corp.
Box 365
Keokuk, IA 52632
(319) 524-3304
Product codes: **AHE   SYA**

Iowa Solar Electronics
P.O. Box 246
North Liberty, IA 52317
(319) 626-2342
Product code: **COC**

Lennox Industries Inc.
350 S. 12th Ave. (P.O. Box 280)

Marshalltown, IA 50158
(515) 754-4011
Product codes: **AHE   AHW   CFL
FEA   SYL   HEP**

NRG Ltd.
901 2nd Ave. East
Coralville, IA 52241
(319) 354-2033
Product codes: **AHE   CCN   AHW**

Pleiad Industries, Inc.
Springdale Rd.
West Branch, IA 52358
(319) 356-2735
Product codes: **AHE   AHW   APO
CFL   FEA**

Solar Electric, Inc.
403 S. Maple
West Branch, IA 52329
(319) 643-2598
Product codes: **AHW   AHE   APO
AMH   AAG   CCN   CCM   CMG
CMA   CMS   CMM   COS   COC
STA   SYA   KIT   FEA   NBS   ASH**

Solar-Thermics Enterprises Ltd.
Highway 34 East (P.O. Box 248)
Creston, IA 50801
(515) 782-8566
Product codes: **AHE   SSF**

Sun Saver Corp.
P.O. Box 276
North Liberty, IA 52317
(319) 626-2343
Product codes: **AHE   APO   AAG
CFA   CCM   CMA   CMM   CMR
COS   COC   STA   STL   SYA   SSF
INS   HEX   KIT   FEA   NBS   LAB
ASH**

United Solar
Box 67
Steamboat Rock, IA 50672
(515) 868-2410
Product codes: **AHE   CFA   SYA
STA   COS   LAB   ASH**

KANSAS

Hydro-Flex Corp.
2101 N.W. Brickyard Rd.
Topeka, KS 66618
(913) 233-7484
Product codes: **CCM   AHC   AHW
APO**

Life Star of Kansas
N. Highway 25

Atwood, KS 67730
Product codes: **AHE   SYA**

Salina Solar Products, Inc.
620 N. 7th
Salina, KS 67401
(913) 823-2131
Product codes: **AHW   CFL   STL
SYL**

Solar Farm Industries, Inc.
P.O. Box 242
Stokton, KS 67669
(913) 425-6726
Product codes: **AHW   AHE   APO
AGH   AMH   AAG   CFA   CCM
CMA   CMH   CMC   COS   COC
KIT   NBS   ASH**

Sunflower Energy Works, Inc.
110 North Main
Hillsboro, KS 67063
(316) 947-5781
Product codes: **CFA   AHE**

KENTUCKY

Kentucky Solar Energies, Inc.
Rt. 1, Box 278
Frankfort, KY 40601
Product codes: **AHW   AHE   APO
CFL   COS   COC   STL   SYL   INS
HEX   FEA   NBS   LAB**

Mid-Western Solar Systems
2235 Irvin Cobb Dr. (Box 2384)
Paducah, KY 42001
(502) 443-6295
Product codes: **AAG   AHE   AHW
CFL   SSF   FEA**

Swedcast Inc.
7350 Empire Dr.
Florence, KY 41042
(606) 283-1501
Product codes: **AHE   AHW   APO
CCM**

LOUISIANA

SEECO (Solar Engrg. & Equip. Co.)
3305 Metairie Rd.
Metairie, LA 70001
(504) 837-0676
Product codes: **AHW   AHE   AAG
CFA   COS   COC   STA   SYA
NBS   ASH**

MAINE
DuMont Industries
Main St.

Monmouth, ME 04259
(207) 933-4281
Product codes: **AHW   SYL   CFL**

Shape Symmetry & Sun, Inc.
Biddeford Industrial Park
Biddeford, ME 04005
(207) 282-6155
Product codes: **AHW   CFL   COS
COC   STL   SYL**

Thornton Sheet Metal
Waterboro, ME 04087
(207) 247-3121
Product codes: **AHE   SSF**

MARYLAND
AAI
P.O. Box 6767
Baltimore, MD 21204
(301) 666-1400
Product codes: **AHC   CCN   FEA**

Belfort Instrument Co.
1600 S. Clinton St.
Baltimore, MD 21224
(301) 342-2626
Product code: **INS**

C & C Solarthermics
P.O. Box 144
Smithburg, MD 21783
(301) 631-1361
Product codes: **AHE   SSF**

KTA Corporation
12300 Washington Ave.
Rockville, MD 20852
(301) 468-2066
Product codes: **AHE   AHW   FEA
CCN   SYL   CTU**

Solar Comfort Systems/Div. Solar Sys.
4853 Cordell Ave. (Suite 606)
Bethesda, MD 20014
(301) 652-8941
Product codes: **AHE   AHW   APO
CFL   SYL   CFA   SYA   STL   COC
KIT   CCM   CMG   FEA**

Solar Energy Systems & Products
500 N. Alley
Emmitsburg, MD 21727
(301) 447-6354
Product codes: **AHE   CFL   AHW
COS**

Solar Industries Ltd.
1727 Llewelyn
Baltimore, MD 21213

(301) 732-2072
Product codes: **AHE   SSF**

N. H. Yates & Co. Inc.
117C Church Lane
Cockeysville, MD 21030
(301) 667-6300
Product codes: **AHE   AHW   CFL
CCM   CMP**

MASSACHUSETTS
Acorn Structures, Inc.
P.O. Box 250
Concord, MA 01742
(617) 369-4111
Product codes: **AHE   AHW   CFL
COS   HEX   STL   SYL**

Columbia Technical Corp./Solar Div.
55 High St.
Holbrook, MA 02343
(617) 767-0513
Product codes: **AHW   APO   CFL
FEA   CFA   COS   STL   SYA
SYL   HEX   AHC**

J. A. Corey, Inc.
60 Woodland St.
West Boylston, MA 01583
(617) 835-3814
Product codes: **AHW   COC**

Daystar Corp.
90 Cambridge St.
Burlington, MA 01803
(617) 272-8460
Product codes: **AHE   AHW   CFL
FEA   SYL   COC   HEX   CMP
CMH**

Dixon Energy Systems, Inc.
47 East St.
Hadley, MA 01035
(413) 584-8831
Product codes: **AHC   AHW   APO
AGH   AMH   AAG   CFL   STL
SYL**

Diy-Sol Inc.
P.O. Box 614
Marlboro, MA 01752
Product codes: **APO   AHE   AHW
KIT   STA   SYA   CFA   CCM
COS   COC   STL   STC**

Elbart Mfg. Co.
127 W. Main St.
Millbury, MA 01527
(617) 865-9412

Product codes: **AHW   CFL   COS
COC   CCM   CMP   STL   SYL**

Calvin T. Frerichs
Chestnut Hill Rd.
Groton, MA 01450
(617) 448-6689
Product codes: **AHW   APO   CFL
CTU   COS   COC   STL   SYL
INS   KIT   LAB**

G.N.S.
79 Magazine St.
Boston, MA 02119
(617) 442-1000
Product codes: **APO   AHC   AAG
CCN   CCM   CMA   CMR   COS
COC   STL   SYL   INS   KIT   NBS
LAB   ASH   AHW**

Itek Corp., Optical Systems Div.
10 Maguire Rd.
Lexington, MA 02117
(617) 276-5825
Product codes: **AHW   APO   CFL
CCM   CMF   CMC   CMR   FEA
NBS   LAB**

Kennecott Copper Corp.
128 Spring St.
Lexington, MA 02173
(617) 862-8268
Product codes: **AHE   AHW   CCM
APO   CMA**

People/Space Co.
259 Marlboro St.
Boston, MA 02109
(617) 742-8652
Product codes: **AHW   AHE   APO
AGH   AMH   CFL   COC   INS
KIT   LAB**

Solafern Ltd.
536 MacArthur Blvd.
Bourne, MA 02532
(617) 563-7181
Product codes: **AHE   AHW   CFA
COS   AAG   STA   SYA   NBS**

Solar Applications, Inc.
One Washington St.
Wellesley, MA 02181
(617) 237-5675
Product codes: **AHW   CFL   SYL
STL**

Solar Aqua Heater Corp.
15 Idlewell St.
Weymouth, MA 02188

(617) 843-7255
Product codes: **CCM   CMR**

Solar Heat Corp.
108 Summer St.
Arlington, MA 02174
(617) 646-5763
Product codes: **AHE   AHW   CFL**

Solargy Systems/Vaughn Corp.
386 Elm St.
Salisbury, MA 01950
(617) 462-6683
Product codes: **AHW   SYL   AHC
APO**

Solarmaster Systems, Inc.
20 Republic Rd.
N. Billerica, MA 01862
(617) 667-4668
Product codes: **AHW   AHE   APO
CFA**

Solectro-Thermo, Inc.
1934 Lakeview Ave.
Dracut, MA 01826
(617) 957-0028
Product codes: **AHW   AHE   APO
CCN   CCM   CMA   CMM   CMT
CMC   CMR   CMB   COS   STA
SYA   NBS   LAB**

Sun Systems, Inc.
P.O. Box 347
Milton, MA 02186
(617) 268-8178
Product codes: **AHE   AHW   CFL
FEA   APO**

Sunkeeper
Box 34, Shawsheen Village Station
Andover, MA 01801
(617) 470-0555
Product codes: **AHW   COC   INS
AHC   COS**

Sunsav Inc.
890 E. St.
Tewksbury, MA 01876
(617) 851-5913
Product codes: **AHC   AHW   CFL
FEA   CCM   CCN   STL   SYL
APO   ACO   ACA   CMG   CMA
CMM   CMC   CMP   CMB   COS
HEP   NBS   ASH**

Vaughn Corp./Solargy
386 Elm St.
Salisbury, MA 01950
(617) 462-6683

Product codes: **AHW   SYL   AHC
APO**

Wescorp
15 Stevens St.
Andover, MA 01810
(617) 470-0520
Product code: **HEP**

MICHIGAN

Addison Products
Addison, MI 49220
(517) 547-6131
Product codes: **AHE   AMH   CFA
COS   STA   SYA**

Champion Home Builders
5573 E. North St.
Dreyden, MI 48428
(313) 796-2211
Product codes: **AHE   SSF   AMH
FEA**

Dow Chemical USA
2020 Dow Center
Midland, MI 48640
(517) 636-3993
Product codes: **AHE   AHW   CCM
CMH   CMS   CMC   CMR   STP**

Electric Motor Repair & Service
Lake Leelanau, MI 49653
(616) 256-9558
Product codes: **AHW   CFL   CCN
CCM   CMP   LAB**

Environmental Energies, Inc.
Box 73, Front St.
Copemish, MI 49625
(616) 378-2000
Product codes: **APO   CFL**

Mueller Brass Co.
Port Huron, MI 48060
(313) 987-4000
Product code: **CCM**

Solar Research
525 N. Fifth St.
Brighton, MI 48116
(313) 227-1151
Product codes: **AHE   AHW   CFL
FEA   APO   CCM   COC   STC
HEX   KIT   CMG**

Solarator, Inc.
P.O. Box 277
Madison Heights, MI 48071
(313) 642-9377

Product codes: AAG   AHC   AGH
AMH   AHW   APO   CFL   SPC

Tranter Inc.
735 E. Hazel St.
Lansing, MI 48909
(517) 372-8410
Product codes: AHE   AHW   CCM
CMA   HEX

Vinyl-Fab Industries
930 E. Drayton
Ferndale, MI 48220
(313) 399-8745
Product codes: APO   SPC

MINNESOTA

A TO Z Solar Products
200 E. 26th St.
Minneapolis, MN 55404
(612) 870-1323
Product codes: AHW   CCM   COC
STC   SYL   INS   KIT

Honeywell Inc.
2600 Ridgeway Rd.
Minneapolis, MN 55413
Product codes: AHC   AHW   APO
CFL   COS   COC

Ilse Engineering
7177 Arrowhead Rd.
Duluth, MN 55811
(218) 729-6858
Product codes: AHE   AHW   APO
CFL   CCM   CMA   STL   SYL
FEA

National Energy Co.
21716 Kendrick Ave.
Lakeville, MN 55044
(612) 469-3401
Product codes: AHE   AHW   CFA
SYA   STA   COS   COC   NBS
FEA   CCM   CMB

Northern Solar Power Co.
311 S. Elm St.
Moorhead, MN 56560
(218) 233-2515
Product codes: AHW   AHE   CFL

Sheldahl/Advanced Products Div.
Northfield, MN 55057
(507) 645-5633
Product codes: AHE   AHW   CCM
CMR

Solar Enterprises, Inc.
7830 N. Beach St.
Minneapolis, MN 55440
(612) 483-8103
Product codes: AHW   AHC   APO
AGH   AMH   AAG   CFL   CCM
CMG   CMA   CMH   CMC   CMP
COS   COC   STL   SYL   HEX
HEP   LAB   ASH

Solargizer Corp.
220 Mulberry St.
Stillwater, MN 55082
(612) 439-5734
Product codes: AHE   AHW   CFL
FEA   APO   SYL   KIT   CCM
CMP   STL

The Lord's Power Co. Inc.
726 Marshall St.
Albert Lea, MN 56007
(507) 377-1820
Product codes: AHE   CFA   SYA   KIT

3-M Co.
Box 33331, Stop 62
St. Paul, MN 55133
Product codes: AHE   AHW   CCM
CMC   CMF

MISSOURI

Chemical Sealing Corp.
5401 Banks Ave.
Kansas City, MO 64130
(816) 923-8812
Product codes: CCM   CMS

Midwest Solar Corp.
2359 Grissom Dr.
St. Louis, MO 63141
(314) 569-3110
Product codes: AHW   AGH   CFA
CCN   STL   SYL   LAB

Suncraft Solar Systems
5001 E. 59th St.
Kansas City, MO 64130
(816) 333-2100
Product codes: AHE   CFA   FEA
STA   SYA   COS

Weather-Made Systems, Inc.
West Hwy 266, Rt. 7, Box 300-D
Springfield, MO 65802
(417) 865-0684
Product codes: AHE   AHW   CFL

Weather-Made Systems, Inc.
Rt. 2, Box 268-S

Lamar, MO 64759
(417) 682-3489
Product codes: **AHE   AHW   CFL**

NEBRASKA

Hot Line Solar, Inc.
P.O. Box 546/1811 Hillcrest Dr.
Bellevue, NE 68005
(402) 291-3888
Product codes: **AHE   CCN**

Lambda Instruments Corp.
4421 Superior St. (P.O. Box 4425)
Lincoln, NE 68504
(402) 467-3576
Product code: **INS**

Solar America, Inc.
9001 Arbor St.
Omaha, NE 68124
(402) 397-2421
Product codes: **AHC   AHW   ACA
AAG   CFL   CFA   STL   SYA
HEP**

Solar Inc.
P.O. Box 246
Mead, NE 68041
(402) 624-6555
Product codes: **AHE   SYA   STP
COS   NBS   FEA**

Solar Utilities of Nebraska—SUN
922 Lake St. (P.O. Box 387)
Gothenburg, NE 69138
(308) 537-7377
Product codes: **AHE   CFA   KIT
COC   AHW   SSF   COS   CCM
CMB**

NEVADA

Richdel Inc.
P.O. Drawer A (1851 Oregon St.)
Carson City, NV 89701
(702) 882-6786
Product codes: **COC   APO   AHW**

Southwest Ener-Tech, Inc.
3030 S. Valley View Blvd.
Las Vegas, NV 89102
(702) 873-1975
Product codes: **AHE   AHW   CFL
FEA**

Sundog Solar
3800 N. Virginia St.
Reno, NV 89506
(702) 322-8080
Product codes: **AHW   AHE   APO**

**AGH   AMH   CFL   CCM   CMA
CMM   COS   STL   SYL   INS
HEX   KIT   LAB**

NEW HAMPSHIRE

Contemporary Systems, Inc.
68 Charlonne St.
Jaffrey, NH 03452
(603) 532-7972
Product codes: **AHE   CFA   FEA
COS   STA   SYA**

Hampshire Controls Corp.
Drawer M
Exeter, NH 03833
(603) 772-5442
Product codes: **COS   COC**

Hollis Observatory
One Pine St.
Nashua, NH 03060
(603) 882-5017
Product code: **INS**

Kalwall Corp., Solar Components Div.
Box 237
Manchester, NH 03105
(603) 668-8186
Product codes: **AHE   APO   CFA
CFL   CCM   STL   STC   SYA
AHW   CMG   SYP   CMA   CMS
CMC   COC   COS   CMB   CMP
SYL**

Natural Power, Inc.
Francestown Turnpike
New Boston, NH 03070
(603) 487-5512
Product codes: **AHE   COS   COC
AHW   APO   AGH   AMH   INS**

RDF Corp.
23 Elm Ave.
Hudson, NH 03051
(603) 882-5195
Product code: **INS**

Solar Sauna
Box 446
Hollis, NH 03049
Product codes: **AHE   AGH   KIT**

Solarmetrics
23 Bridge St.
Manchester, NH 03101
(603) 668-3216
Product codes: **COS   COC   STA
STL   INS   AHC   AHW   APO**

Sunhouse Inc.
6 Southgate Dr.
Nashua, NH 03060
(603) 888-0953
Product codes: **AHC   AHW   CFL
SYL**

Urethane Molding, Inc.
Route 11
Laconia, NH 03246
(603) 524-7577
Product codes: **AHE   AHW   CCM**

NEW JERSEY

Aerco International, Inc.
159 Paris Ave.
Northvale, NJ 07697
(201) 768-2400
Product code: **HEX**

Allied Chemical, Fibers Div.
P.O. Box 1057R
Morristown, NJ 07960
(201) 455-2000
Product codes: **CCM   CMG**

American Solar Companies, Inc.
Bldg. #4, Ford Rd.
Denville, NJ 07834
(201) 627-0021
Product codes: **FEA   LAB   AHC
AGH   COC   STL   INS   HEX
HEP   KIT   AHE   AHW   APO
SYL**

American Solarize, Inc.
P.O. Box 15
Martinsville, NJ 08836
(201) 356-3141
Product codes: **AHE   CFA   COS
STL   STA   SYA   STP**

Berry Solar Products
Woodbridge at Main (P.O. Box 327)
Edison, NJ 08817
(201) 549-3800
Product codes: **CCM   CMC**

Burling Instrument Corp.
P.O. Box 298
Chatham, NJ 07928
(201) 635-9481
Product codes: **AHW   AHE   INS**

Calmac Mfg. Corp.
P.O. Box 710E
Englewood, NJ 07631
(201) 569-0420
Product codes: **AHE   AHW   CFL
FEA   APO   STP   KIT**

Climatrol Corp.
Woodbridge Ave.
Edison, NJ 08812
(201) 549-7200
Product codes: **AHC   AMH   CFL
COS   COC   STL   SYL   HEX
HEP   NBS   LAB   ASH**

Creighton Solar Concepts
662 Whitehead Rd.
Lawrenceville, NJ 08648
(609) 587-6527
Product codes: **AHW   CFL**

CY/RO Industries
Wayne, NJ 07470
(201) 839-4800
Product codes: **AGH   CCM   CMG
SYP**

Drew Chemical Corp.
1 Drew Chemical Plaza
Boonton, NJ 07005
(201) 263-7600
Product codes: **CCM   CMH   CMI**

Edwards Engineering Corp.
101 Alexander Ave.
Pompton Plains, NJ 07444
(201) 835-2808
Product codes: **AHC   AHW   APO
SYL**

**H & H Thermostats Div.,
Emerson Electric**
25 Canfield Rd.
Cedar Grove, NJ 07009
(201) 239-1331
Product codes: **AHW   AHE   COC**

HCH Associates, Inc.
P.O. Box 87
Robbinsville, NJ 08691
(609) 259-9722
Product codes: **AHE   AHW   CCM
CMG**

Heilemann Electric
127 Mountain View Rd.
Warren, NJ 07060
(201) 757-4507
Product codes: **CFL   HEX   STL
CTU   COC   AHW   AHE   APO**

New Jersey Aluminum, Solar Div.
1007 Jersey Ave. (P.O. Box 73)
North Brunswick, NJ 08902
(201) 249-6867
Product codes: **CCM   CMA   KIT
AHE   AHW**

Ominidata, Inc.
16 Springdale Rd.
Cherry Hill, NJ 08003
(609) 424-4646
Product code: **INS**

Science Associates, Inc.
230 Nassau St. (P.O. Box 230)
Princeton, NJ 08540
(609) 924-4470
Product code: **INS**

Solar Energy Systems, Inc.
One Olney Ave.
Cherry Hill, NJ 08003
(609) 424-4446
Product codes: **AHW   CFL   FEA
COS   STL   SYL   AHC   APO
HEP**

Solar Equipment Corp.
Woodbridge at Main (P.O. Box 327)
Edison, NJ 08817
(201) 549-3800
Product codes: **CCM   CMA   CMC**

Solar Heating of New Jersey
811 Wynetta Place
Paramus, NJ 07652
(201) 652-3819
Product codes: **CFL   COC   AHW
AHE   APO   CCM   CMR**

Solar Industries Inc.
Monmouth Airport Industrial Park
Farmingdale, NJ 07727
(201) 938-7000
Product codes: **APO   SYL   CFL
COC**

Solar Life
404 Lippincott Ave.
Riverton, NJ 08077
(609) 829-7022
Product codes: **AHW   SYL**

Solar Living, Inc.
P.O. Box 12
Netcong, NJ 07857
(201) 691-8483
Product codes: **AHW   CFL   CCM
CMA   KIT**

Solec
Dept. DM
P.O. Box 3065
Princeton, NJ 08540
Product code: **INS**

SSP Associates
704 Blue Hill Rd.
River Vale, NJ 07675
(201) 391-4724
Product codes: **AHE   AHW   CFL   CTU**

C. W. Thornthwaite Assoc.
Route 1/Centerton
Elmer, NJ 08318
(609) 358-2350
Product code: **INS**

Trol-a-Temp
725 Federal Ave.
Kenilworth, NJ 07033
(201) 245-3190
Product codes: **AHE   AHW   COS**

Universal Power, Inc.
P.O. Box 339
Island Heights, NJ 08732
(201) 928-2828
Product codes: **AHE   AMH   CFA
COS   COC   SYA**

W & W Solar Systems, Inc.
399 Mill St.
Rahway, NJ 07065
(201) 925-5488
Product codes: **AHE   AHW   APO
CFL**

NEW MEXICO

**Albuquerque Western Solar
Industries Inc.**
612 Commanche, N.E.
Albuquerque, NM 87107
(505) 3435-6764
Product codes: **AHC   CCN   FEA
SYL**

K-Line Corp.
911 Penn. Ave. N.E.
Albuquerque, NM 87110
(505) 268-3379
Product codes: **AHE   CFA   STA
SYA   AHW   COS   INS**

Sigma Energy Products
720 Rankin Rd. N.E.
Albuquerque, NM 87107
(505) 344-3431
Product codes: **AHE   AHW   APO
CFL   FEA**

Solar Room Co.
Box 1377
Taos, NM 97511
(505) 758-9344
Product codes: **AHE   AGH   KIT**

Soltrax Inc.
720 Rankin Rd. N.E.
Albuquerque, NM 87107
(505) 344-3431
Product codes: **AHW   APO   AHC
ACA   AAG   CFL   CCN   COS
COC   STL   SYL   KIT   LAB**

Southwest—STANDARD
P.O. Box 14132
Albuquerque, NM 87111
(505) 265-8871
Product codes: **CFL   AHW   APO
NBS**

United States Solar Pillow
P.O. Box 987
Tucumcari, NM 88401
(505) 461-2608
Product codes: **APO   CFL   FEA
SYP   SYA   SYL   CFA   AHC
AGH   AAG**

Zomeworks Industries
P.O. Box 712
Albuquerque, NM 87103
(505) 242-5354
Product codes: **SYP   AHC   AHW
SYL   SYA   CCM   CMR   CMT
KIT   FEA**

NEW YORK

Advance Cooler Mfg. Corp.
Rt. 146, Bradford Industrial Pk.
Clifton Park, NY 12065
(518) 371-2140
Product codes: **AHW   CFL   FEA
CCM   COC   STL   STA   SYA
SYL   SYP   AHC**

American Acrylic Corp.
173 Marine St.
Farmingdale, NY 11735
(516) CH9-1129
Product codes: **AHE   AHW   APO
CCM   CMG**

Amprobe Instruments
630 Merrick Rd.
Lynbrook, NY 11563
Product code: **INS**

Bio-Energy Systems, Inc.
Mountaindale Rd.
Spring Glen, NY 12483
(914) 434-7858
Product codes: **AHE   AHW   APO
AGH   AAG   CFL   CFA   COS
STA   STL   SYA   SYL   SYP   KIT**

Bi-Hex Co.
P.O. Box 312
Bedford, NY 10506
(914) 764-4021
Product codes: **COS   COC**

Catalano & Sons, Inc.
301 Stagg St.
Brooklyn, NY 11206
(212) 821-6100
Product codes: **AHE   AHW   CFL
SYL   COC**

Conkling Laboratories
5432 Merrick Rd.
Massapequa, NY 11758
(516) 541-13323
Product code: **INS**

Ecosol Ltd.
2 W. 59th St. (17th Fl.), The Plaza
New York, NY 10019
(212) 838-6170
Product codes: **AHC   AHW   COS
HEP   INS**

Ford Products Corp.
Ford Products Rd.
Valley Cottage, NY 10989
(914) 358-8282
Product codes: **AHW   STL**

**Grumman Corp., Energy Sys. Div.
(Dept. G-R)**
4175 Veterans Memorial Highway
Ronkonkoma, NY 11779
(516) 575-6205
Product codes: **AHE   AHW   CFL
FEA   SYL   APO   CCM   CMH
CMP**

Hitachi Chemical Co., Ltd.
437 Madison Ave.
New York, NY 10022
(212) 838-4804
Product codes: **AHW   APO   CFL
STL   SYL   COC   CMP   CCM**

Hudson Valley Solar
Box 388/Rt. 9
Valatie, NY 12184
(518) 781-4152
Product codes: **AHE   SSF**

Mechanical Mirror Works
661 Edgecombe Ave.
New York, NY 10032
(212) 795-2100
Product codes: **AHC   CCM   CMR**

Prima Industries, Inc.
P.O. Box 141
Deer Park, NY 11729
(516) 242-6347
Product codes: **AHW   CFL   SYL**

Ran Solar Energy Products, Inc.
50 Peabrook Ave.
Deer Park, NY 11729
(516) 586-5008
Product codes: **APO   CFL   SYL**

Revere Copper & Brass, Inc.
P.O. Box 151
Rome, NY 13440
(315) 338-2401
Product codes: **AHW   CFL   FEA
APO   CCM   SYL   COS   COC
AHE   STL   CMP   NBS**

Solar Energy Systems, Inc.
Concord House (Suite 2B),
P.O. Box 625
Scarsdale, NY 10583
(914) 725-5570
Product codes: **AHW   AHC   APO
ACA   AMH   CFL   CCM   CMH
SYA   SYL   SYP   KIT   NBS**

Solar Sunstill, Inc.
15 Blueberry Ridge Rd.
Setauket, NY 11733
(516) 941-4078
Product codes: **CCM   CMC   CMR**

Standard Solar Collectors, Inc.
1465 Gates Ave.
Brooklyn, NY 11227
(212) 456-1882
Product codes: **AHW   AHE   CFA
CFL   STL   SYA   SYL   KIT   FEA
ASH**

Structured Sheets, Inc.
196 E. Camp Ave.
Merrick, NY 11566
(516) 546-4868
Product codes: **AHE   AGH   CCM
CMG**

Sun Chance
P.O. Box 506
South Fallsburg, NY 12779
(914) 434-6650
Product codes: **AHW   CTU   CCM
CMT   CMP   COS**

Sunergy Power, Ltd.
400 W. Main St.
Babylon, NY 11072

(516) 587-0611
Product codes: **AHE   APO   CFA
CFL**

Sunray Solar Heat, Inc.
202 Classon Ave.
Brooklyn, NY 11205
(212) 857-0193
Product codes: **AHW   AHE   APO
AMH   CFL   COS   SYL   KIT**

Temp-O-Matic Cooling Co.
87 Luquer St.
Brooklyn, NY 11231
(212) 624-5600
Product codes: **AHE   AHW   CFL
FEA**

Union Carbide Corp.
270 Park Ave.
New York, NY 10017
(212) 551-2261
Product codes: **CCM   CMA**

Weksler Instruments Corp.
80 Mill Rd. (P.O. Box 3040)
Freeport, NY 11520
(516) 623-0100
Product code: **COC**

NORTH CAROLINA

Carolina Aluminum
State Rd. 1184/P.O. Box 2437
Burlington, NC 27215
(919) 227-8826
Product code: **CCM**

Carolina Aluminum
Metcalf Rd. (Box 177)
Winton, NC 27986
(919) 358-5811
Product code: **CCM**

Carolina Solar Equipment Co.
P.O. Box 2068
Salisbury, NC 28144
(704) 637-1243
Product codes: **AHE   AHW   CFL
FEA   SYL**

Carolina Thermal Co.
Iron Works Rd., Rt. 2, Box 39
Reidsville, NC 27320
(919) 342-0352
Product codes: **AGH   CFA**

Energy Applications, Inc.
Route 5, P.O. Box 383
Rutherfordton, NC 28139
(704) 287-2195

Product codes: **AHC   CCN   CCM
CMT   COC   CMM**

Habitat 2000 Inc.
P.O. Box 188
Belmont, NC 28012
(704) 825-5357
Product codes: **AHW   AHE   APO
AGH   STL   SYL   HEX   KIT**

Jensen Solar, Inc.
P.O. Box 166
Goldsboro, NC 27530
(919) 566-4320
Product codes: **AHW   CFL   SYL**

McArthurs, Inc.
P.O. Box 236
Forest City, NC 28043
(704) 245-7223
Product codes: **AHE   AHW   AAG
CFA   CFL   SYP**

Solar Comfort Inc.
Route 3, Box 139
Statesville, NC 28677
(704) 872-0753
Product codes: **AHE   SSF**

Solar Development & Mfg. Co.
4000 Old Wake Forest Rd.
Raleigh, NC 27609
(919) 872-6900
Product codes: **AHE   AHW   CCN
STL   SYL   COS**

Standard Electric Co.
P.O. Box 631
Rocky Mount, NC 27801
(919) 442-1155
Product codes: **AHE   AHW   CFL
FEA**

OHIO

Alpha Solarco
1014 Vine St., Suite 2230, Kroger Bldg.
Cincinnati, OH 45202
(513) 621-1243
Product codes: **LAB   AHE   CCN
CFL   CFE**

Ferro Corp., Coatings Div.
P.O. Box 6550, 4150 E. 56th St.
Cleveland, OH 44101
(216) 641-8580
Product codes: **CCM   CMC**

Fiber-Rite Products
P.O. Box 9295
Cleveland, OH 44138

(216) 228-2921
Product codes: **STL   STC   KIT
AHW   AHE**

General Solar Systems
4040 Lake Park Rd. (Box 2687)
Youngstown, OH 44507
(216) 783-0270
Product codes: **AHE   CCN   CCM
CMM**

Glass-Lined Water Heater Co.
13000 Athens Ave.
Cleveland, OH 44107
(216) 521-1377
Product codes: **AHW   STL**

Lof Solar Energy Systems
1701 Broadway
Toledo, OH 43605
(419) 247-4355
Product codes: **AHE   AHW   CFL
FEA   CCM   CMG   COC   COS**

Mid-West Technology, Inc.
P.O. Box 26238
Dayton, OH 45426
(513) 274-6020
Product codes: **AHE   CCM   CMA**

Mor-Flo Industries, Inc.
18450 S. Miles Rd.
Cleveland, OH 44128
(216) 663-7300
Product codes: **AHW   SYL   STL
CFL   KIT   CCM   CMH   CMI
CMM   HEX**

NRG Manufacturing
P.O. Box 53
Napoleon, OH 43545
(419) 599-3618
Product codes: **AHE   SSF   FEA**

Ohio Valley Solar, Inc.
4141 Airport Rd.
Cincinnati, OH 45226
(513) 871-1961
Product codes: **AHE   APO   CFA
COS   STA   SYA   LAB   SSF**

Owens Illinois, Inc.
P.O. Box 1035
Toledo, OH 43666
(419) 242-6543
Product codes: **AHC   CTU   FEA
AHW**

Ranco Inc.
601 W. Fifth Ave.

Columbus, OH 43201
Product codes: **AHE   AHW   COC**

Solar Central
7213 Ridge Road
Mechanicsburg, OH 43044
(513) 828-1350
Product codes: **AHW   CFL   FEA
CCM   HEP   AHC   KIT   SYL
STL   CMP   COS   AGH   ACA
SYP   RCE   CMM   CMG**

Solar Energy Products Co.
121 Miller Rd.
Avon Lake, OH 44012
(216) 933-5000
Product codes: **AHE   AHW   FEA
HEX   APO   SYA   COC   STA
CFA   AAG   CCM   CMB**

Solar Glo-Thermal Energy Systems, Inc.
P.O. Box 377
Dayton, OH 45459
(513) 252-6150
EXTENSIVE PRODUCT LINE

Solar Heat Corp.
1252 French Ave.
Lakewood, OH 44107
(216) 228-2993
Product codes: **AHE   AHW   CFL
FEA   KIT**

Solar Home Systems, Inc.
12931 W. Geauga Trail
Chesterland, OH 44026
(216) 729-9350
Product codes: **AHW   APO   AHE
CFL   CFA   COC   STA   SYA
SYL   NBS   ASH**

Solar Sun Inc.
235 W. 12th St.
Cincinnati, OH 45210
(513) 241-4200
Product codes: **AHE   AHW   APO
CFL   SYL**

Solar Usage Now, Inc.
450 E. Tiffin St./P.O. Box 306
Bascom, OH 44809
(419) 937-2226
Product codes: **AHW   CFL   KIT**

Solar 1/Div. Stellar Industries, Inc.
7265 Commerce Dr.
Mentor, OH 44060
(216) 951-6363
Product codes: **AHW   AHE   APO
CFA   COS   COC   STA   SYA**

INS   FEA   NBS   ASH

Solartec Inc.
250 Penn. Ave.
Salem, OH 44460
(216) 332-9100
Product codes: **AHW   AGH   CFA
CCM   CMA   CMM   COC   STL
HEX   NBS   LAB   ASH**

Sol-Era Energy Systems
P.O. Box 651
Worthington, OH 43085
(614) 846-8594
Product codes: **AHW   AHE   APO
CFL   STL   SYL   STA**

Stolle Corp.
1501 Michigan St.
Sidney, OH 45365
(513) 492-1111
Product codes: **AHW   AHE   CFL
STL   SYL   HEX   NBS   ASH**

Van Hussel Tube Corp.
Warren, OH 44481
(216) 372-8221
Product codes: **CCM   CMA**

Yellow Springs Instrument Co.
Yellow Springs, OH 45387
(513) 767-7241
Product code: **INS**

OKLAHOMA

Anabil Enterprizes
525 S. Aqua Clear Dr.
Mustang, OK 73064
(405) 376-3324
Product codes: **COS   COC**

Brown Mfg. Co.
P.O. Box 14546
Oklahoma City, OK 73114
(405) 751-1323
Product codes: **AHW   COS   SYP
AHC   COC**

Coating Laboratories
505 S. Quaker
Tulsa, OK 74120
(918) 272-1191
Product codes: **CCM   CMR**

McKim Solar Energy Systems, Inc.
2627 E. Admiral Place
Tulsa, OK 74110
(918) 936-4035
Product codes: **AHC   AHW   APO
CFA   CFL   CTU   CCN   CCM**

(Products continued)

CMT COS COC STA STL
STP HEX KIT NBS LAB ASH

Professional Fiberglass Products, Inc.
ADA Industrial Park (P.O. Box 1179)
Ada, OK 74820
(405) 436-0223
Product code: STL

Westinghouse Electric Corp.
5005 Interstate Dr. North
Norman, OK 73069
(405) 364-4040
Product code: HEP

OREGON
Kastek Corp.
P.O. Box 8881
Portland, OR 97208
Product codes: APO AHW AAG
CFL SYL

Solar Kits
P.O. Box 350
Philomath, OR 97370
(503) 929-6289
Product codes: AHW APO CFL
KIT

Solar Pre-Fab Ltd.
2625 S.E. Kelley St.
Portland, OR 97202
(503) 233-1652
Product codes: AHW CFL KIT

Sun Life Solar Products
12900 S.E. 32nd Ave.
Milwaukee, OR 97222
(503) 653-1449
Product codes: AHC AHW CFL
STL SYL

Sun Power Corp.
12785 S.E. Hiway 212
Portland, OR 97015
(503) 655-6282
Product codes: AHC AHW APO
CFE

Tektronix Products
P.O. Box 500
Beaverton, OR 97077
(503) 644-0161
Product code: LAB

PENNSYLVANIA
Alco Plastic Products
266 Delray Ave.
Hanover, PA 17331

Product codes: AHE CCM SYP
CMG

Aluminum Co. of America
Alcoa Bldg.
Pittsburgh, PA 15219
(412) 553-2321
Product codes: CCM APO SYL
COC CMA CMC CMM CFL
AHE AHW FEA

Ametek Inc.
1 Spring Ave.
Hatfield, PA 19440
(215) 822-2971
Product codes: AHW CFL FEA
AHC NBS LAB

Amicks Solar Heating
375 Aspen St.
Middletown, PA 17057
(717) 944-1842
Product codes: AHE AHW APO
CFL CTU CCM CMG CMA
CMH CMC CMS CMP COC
STL SYL HEX

Atlas Vinyl Products
7002 Beaver Dam Rd.
Levittown, PA 19057
(215) 946-3620
Product codes: APO CFL FEA

Carlisle Tile & Rubber Co.
P.O. Box 99
Carlisle, PA 17013
(717) 249-1000
Product codes: AHW AHE STC

Electro-Kinetic Systems, Inc.
2500 E. Ridley Ave.
Chester, PA 19013
(215) 876-6192
Product codes: CCM CMC

Energy Systems Products, Inc.
12th & Market St.
Lemoyne, PA 17043
(717) 761-8130
Product codes: CCM CMM CMH

Enviropane Inc.
350 N. Marshall St.
Lancaster, PA 17602
(717) 299-3737
Product codes: AHE AHW CFL
FEA CFA CCM CMA

Foam Products, Inc.
Gay St.

York Haven, PA 17370
(717) 266-3671
Product codes: **AHE   CFA   STA
SSF   FEA   NBS**

General Electric Co.
P.O. Box 13601/Bldg. #7
Philadelphia, PA 19101
(215) 962-2112
Product codes: **AHW   AHC   CTU
SYL   HEP   CCM   CMG**

Heliotherm Inc.
W. Lenni Rd.
Lenni, PA 19052
(215) 459-9030
Product codes: **AHE   AHW   CFL
FEA   SYL**

International Environment Corp.
1400 Mill Creek Rd.
Gladwyne, PA 19035
(215) 642-3060
Product codes: **AHW   CFL   FEA
AHE   SYL**

Overly Mfg. Co.
574 W. Otterman St.
Greensburg, PA 15601
(412) 834-7300
Product codes: **AHE   AHW   APO
CFL**

Packless Industries Inc.
P.O. Box 310
Mount Wolf, PA 17347
Product codes: **AHW   HEX   APO
AHC**

PPG Industries
One Gateway Center
Pittsburgh, PA 15222
(412) 434-3555
Product codes: **AHE   AHW   CFL
FEA   APO**

Practical Solar Heating
209 S. Delaware Dr., Rt. 611
Easton, PA 18042
(215) 252-6381
Product codes: **AHE   COC   CFL
STC   APO   KIT   CCM   AHW
HEX   STL   CMP   CTU**

Pyco
600 E. Lincoln Hwy.
Penndel, PA 19047
(215) 757-3704
Product code: **INS**

Rohn & Haas, Plastics Engineering
P.O. Box 219
Bristol, PA 19007
(215) 788-5501
Product codes: **CCM   CMG   CMS**

Milton Roy Co., Hartell Div.
70 Industrial Dr.
Ivyland, PA 18974
(215) 322-0730
Product codes: **CCM   CMP**

**Simons Solar Environmental
Systems, Inc.**
24 Carlisle Pike
Mechanicsburg, PA 17055
(717) 697-2778
Product codes: **AHW   SYL   AHE
CFL   CCM   COS   KIT   COC
CMA   CMG   CMP   FEA**

Solar Energy Assoc.
1063 New Jersey Ave.
Hellertown, PA 18055
(215) 838-7460
Product codes: **AHW   CFL**

Solar Mfg. Co.
40 Conneaut Lake Rd.
Greenville, PA 16125
(412) 588-2571
Product codes: **AHE   CFA   CCM
STA   SYA   COS   CMG   SSF   FEA**

Solar Power Inc.
201 Airport Blvd., Cross Keys
Doylestown, PA 18901
(215) 348-9066
Product codes: **AHE   SSF**

Solar Shelter Engineering Co.
P.O. Box 179
Kutztown, PA 19530
(215) 683-6769
Product codes: **AHE   SSF   FEA
AHW   CFA   COS   STA   SYA
STP   NBS   ASH**

Sun God
P.O. Box 54
New Britain, PA 18901
(215) 368-7719
Product codes: **AHW   CFL   COS
COC   HEX**

Sundevelopment Inc.
1108 Hanover Rd.
York, PA 17404
(717) 225-5066
Product codes: **AHE   AHW   CFL**

Sunearth Solar Products Corp.
R.D. 1, Box 337
Green Lane, PA 18054
(215) 699-7892
Product codes: **AHE   AHW   CFL
FEA   CCM   SYL   STL   CMA
CMG   CMH   CMS   CMM   CMP
COC   COS**

Sunwall Inc.
P.O. Box 9723
Pittsburgh, PA 15229
(412) 364-5349
Product codes: **AHE   AHW   APO
CFA   FEA   STA   STL   SYA
SYL   SYP   KIT**

PUERTO RICO

Solar Devices Inc.
GPO BOH 3727
San Juan, PR 00936
(809) 783-1775
Product codes: **AHW   CFL   SYL**

RHODE ISLAND

Eppley Laboratory Inc.
12 Sheffield Ave.
Newport, RI 02840
(401) 847-1020
Product code: **INS**

Independent Energy, Inc.
P.O. Box 363
Kingston, RI 02881
(401) 295-1762
Product code: **COC**

Solar Homes, Inc.
2707 S. County Trail
East Greenwich, RI 02818
(401) 294-2443
Product codes: **AHE   AHW   CFL
CFA**

Solar Products, Inc.
12 Hylestead St.
Providence, RI 02905
(401) 467-7350
Product codes: **AHW   AHE   CFL
SYL**

TACO Inc.
1160 Cranston St.
Cranston, RI 02920
(401) 942-8000
Product codes: **HEX   COS   COC
CCM   CMP**

SOUTH CAROLINA

General Solargenic Corp.
P.O. Box 307
Johns Island, SC 29455
(803) 747-4480
Product codes: **AHC   AHW   CFA
STA   SYA   KIT**

Helio Thermics Inc.
110 Laurens Rd.
Greenville, SC 29601
(803) 235-8529
Product codes: **AHE   SYA**

Solar Energy Research & Development
302 Lucas
Mt. Pleasant, SC 29464
(803) 884-0290
Product codes: **AHW   AHE   CFL
COS   STL   SYL**

Sunsaver Inc.
P.O. Box 21672
Columbia, SC 29221
(803) 781-4962
Product codes: **AHW   AGH   CFL
STL   SYL   HEX   KIT**

SOUTH DAKOTA

The Solar Stor
No. 1 Solar Lane
Parker, SD 57053
(605) 648-3465
Product codes: **AHE   SSF**

TENNESSEE

ASG Industries
P.O. Box 929
Kingsport, TN 37662
(615) 245-0211
Product codes: **AHW   APO   CCM   AHC**

Energy Converters Inc.
2501 N. Orchard Knob Ave.
Chattanooga, TN 37406
(615) 624-2608
Product codes: **AHE   AHW   CFL   FEA**

Energy Design Corp.
Box 34294
Memphis, TN 38134
(901) 382-3000
Product codes: **AHW   CCN   AHC**

W. L. Jackson Mfg. Co.
1200-26 W. 40th St.
Chattanooga, TN 37401
(615) 867-4700
Product codes: **AHE   SYL   CFL**

State Industries Inc.
Cumberland St.
Ashland City, TN 37015
(615) 792-4371   .
Product codes: **AHE   AHW   CFL
FEA   SYL   STL   KIT**

TEXAS

Ace Solar Systems
Rt. 1/Box 50
Mission, TX 78572
(512) 585-6353
Product codes: **AHE   AHW   CFL
SYP**

American Solar King Corp.
6801 New McGregor Highway
Waco, TX 76710
(817) 776-3860
Product codes: **AHE   AHW   CFL
FEA**

Butler Vent-a-Matic Corp.
P.O. Box 728
Mineral Wells, TX 76067
(800) 433-1626
Product codes: **APO   AHW   SYL
AHE   CFL   HEX**

Cole Solar Systems, Inc.
440A E. St. Elmo Rd.
Austin, TX 78745
(512) 444-2565
Product codes: **AHW   APO   CFL
SYL   CCM   CMM   FEA**

Denton Greenhouse Mfg. Inc.
3301 Fortworth
Denton, TX 76201
(817) 382-1107
Product code: **AGH**

Dodge Products
Box 19781
Houston, TX 77024
(713) 467-6262
Product code: **INS**

Exxon Company USA
P.O. Box 2180
Houston, TX 77001
(713) 656-0370
Product codes: **AHC   AHW   CCM
CMH**

Friedrich Air Cond./Refrigeration
P.O. Box 1540
San Antonio, TX 78295
(512) 225-2000
Product codes: **AHE   HEP**

Greenhouse Systems Corp.
P.O. Box 31407
Dallas, TX 75231
(214) 352-6174
Product codes: **AHE   AAG   CBL**

Grow House Corp.
5881 Prestonview, Suite 156
Dallas, TX 75240
Product codes: **CCM   SYP   CMG
AGH**

Northrup Inc.
302 Nichols Dr.
Hutchins, TX 75141
(214) 225-4291
Product codes: **AHC   AHW   CFL
CCN   FEA   APO**

P C A
11031 Wye Dr.
San Antonio, TX 78217
(512) 656-9338
Product codes: **NBS   STL   CCM
APO   AHW   AHE   CFL   SYL
KIT   CMP**

Shell Oil Co.
1 Shell Plaza (P.O. Box 2463)
Houston, TX 77001
Product codes: **AHC   CCM   CMH**

Solar Control Corp.
P.O. Box 2201 (201 W FM 2410)
Harker Heights, TX 76541
(817) 699-8858
Product codes: **AHW   AHE   CFA
CFL   CCN**

Solar Enterprises, Inc.
2816 W. Div.
Arlington, TX 76012
(817) 461-5571
Product codes: **AHE   CCM   CMA
CMM   CMC   COS   COC   STL
HEX   KIT   FEA   ASH   AHW
APO   CFL   SYL**

Solar Kinetics, Inc.
147 Parkhouse St. (P.O. Box 10764)
Dallas, TX 75207
(214) 747-6519
Product codes: **AHE   AHW   CCN
FEA**

Solar Therm
203 Point Royal Dr.
Rockwall, TX 75087
(214) 475-2201
Product codes: **AHE   AHW   APO**

(Products continued)

CFL   CCM   CMM   KIT   CMA
CMG   STL   CMP   CMI   COC

Solarsystems Inc.
507 W. Elm St.
Tyler, TX 75702
(214) 592-5343
Product codes: AHC   AHW   APO
CFE   FEA   NBS

Solartech Systems Corp.
Box 591
Devine, TX 78016
(512) 663-4491
Product codes: AHE   AHW   APO
CFL   SYL   NBS

Soltex Corp.
1804 Afton St., Lock Lane
Houston, TX 77055
(713) 782-4478
Product codes: AHE   AHW   CFL
FEA

Solus Inc.
P.O. Box 35227
Houston, TX 77035
(713) 772-6416
Product codes: AHW   AHC   APO
AAG   CFL   SYL   HEP

Southwest-Standard
P.O. Box 10094
El Paso, TX 79991
(915) 533-6291
Product codes: CFL   AHW   APO
NBS

Teledyne Geotech
3401 Shiloh Rd.
Garland, TX 75041
(214) 271-2561
Product code: INS

Texas Electronics, Inc.
5529 Redfield St.
Dallas, TX 75209
(214) 631-2490
Product code: INS

Thermon Mfg. Co.
100 Thermon Dr.
San Marcos, TX 78666
(516) 392-5801
Product codes: CCM   CMA   AHE
AHW

Wilshire Foam Products, Inc.
P.O. Box 34217
Dallas, TX 75234

(214) 241-4073
Product code: SPC

UTAH

Griep Heating
155 E. 3600 South
Salt Lake City, UT 84115
(801) 262-2537
Product codes: AHE   AHW   CFA

Permaloy Corp.
P.O. Box 1559
Ogden, UT 84402
Product codes: AHE   CCM   CMC

VERMONT

Garden Way Laboratories
P.O. Box 66
Charlotte, VT 05445
(802) 425-2147
Product codes: SYP   AGH   AHE

Green Mountain Homes
Royalton, VT 05068
(802) 763-8384
Product codes: AHC   SYP   HYB

Solar Alternative, Inc.
30 Clark St.
Brattleboro, VT 05301
(802) 254-8221
Product codes: AHE   AHW   CFL
APO

VIRGINIA

Clark's Products & Services
Route 1/P.O. Box 213B
Bluemont, VA 22012
(703) 955-3837
Product codes: AHW   AHE   APO
CFL   KIT

Corillium Corp./Cronagold Div.
Reston International Center
Reston, VA 22090
(703) 860-2100
Product codes: AHE   CCM   CMC

Helios Corp.
2120 Angus Rd.
Charlottesville, VA 22901
(804) 977-3719
Product codes: AHC   AHW   SYA
SYL   FEA

Intertechnology/Solar Corp. of America
100 Main St.
Warrenton, VA 22186
(703) 347-7900

Product codes: **AHW   CFL   SYL
KIT   AHC   APO   CCN   FEA**

Martin Processing, Inc.
P.O. Box 5068
Martinsville, VA 24112
(703) 629-1711
Product codes: **AGH AAG CCM CMG**

One Design, Inc.
Mountain Falls Route
Winchester, VA 22601
(703) 662-4898
Product code: **SYP**

Pioneer Energy Products
Route 1/P.O. Box 189
Forest, VA 24551
(804) 239-9020
Product codes: **AHW   AHC   CFL
COS   SYL   NBS**

PUFF
920 Allied St.
Charlottesville, VA 22901
(804) 977-3541
Product codes: **AHW   AHE   STL**

Reynolds Metals Co.
P.O. Box 27003
Richmond, VA 23261
(804) 282-3026
Product codes: **AHE   AHW   CFL
FEA   APO   NBS**

Solar Corp. of America/Intertechnology
100 Main St.
Warrenton, VA 22186
(703) 347-7900
Product codes: **AHE   AHW   CFL
FEA   SYL   APO   KIT**

Solar Energy Co.
P.O. Box 649
Gloucester Point, VA 23062
Product codes: **AHE   AHW   APO
CFL**

Solar One Ltd.
2644 Barret St.
Virginia Beach, VA 23451
(804) 340-7774
Product codes: **AHE   STA   SYA
CFA   FEA**

Solar Sensor System
4220 Berritt St.
Fairfax, VA 22030
(703) 273-2683
Product codes: **AHE   COC   AHW
APO   COS   INS**

Virginia Solar Components, Inc.
Route 3/Highway 29 South
Rustburg, VA 24588
(804) 239-9523
Product codes: **AHW   AHC   APO
CFL   CCM   CMP   STL   SYL
COS   COC   INS**

WASHINGTON

E&K Service Co.
16824 74th Ave. N.E.
Bothell, WA 98011
(206) 486-6660
Product codes: **AHE   AHW   CFL
FEA   SYL**

Floscan Instrument Co.
3016 N.E. Blakely St.
Seattle, WA 98105
(206) 524-6625
Product code: **INS**

Mann-Russell Electronics, Inc.
1401 Thorne Rd.
Tacoma, WA 98421
(206) 383-1591
Product codes: **AHE   CCM   CMM
HEL   KIT**

Northwest Solar Systems, Inc.
7700 12th N.E.
Seattle, WA 98115
(206) 523-3951
Product codes: **AHE   AHW   APO
CFA   COC   STA   SYA**

Silverdale Fuel
P.O. Box 37
Silverdale, WA 98383
(206) 692-9221
Product codes: **AHW   APO   ACO
CFA   CCM   SYA   HEX**

Solar Northwest Corp.
Route 1/P.O. Box 114
Long Beach, WA 98631
(206) 642-2249
Product codes: **AHW   COS**

Sun Power Northwest
16615 76th Ave. N.E.
Bothell, WA 98011
(206) 486-6632
Product codes: **AHW   AHC   APO
CFA   CCM   CMC   CMB   COS
STA   SYA   HEX**

Sunpower Industries, Inc.
10837 B6 S.E. 200th
Kent, WA 98031

(206) 854-0670
Product codes: **AHE   CFA   SYA
KIT**

Vertrex Corp.
208 Carlson Bldg., 808-106th N.E.
Bellevue, WA 98004
Product codes: **AHE   COC**

WISCONSIN

Ark-Tic-Seal Systems, Inc.
P.O. Box 428
Butler, WI 53007
(414) 276-0711
Product codes: **AHC   SYP**

Research Products Corp.
P.O. Box 1467
(1015 E. Washington Ave.)
Madison, WI 53701
(608) 257-8801
Product codes: **AHW   AHE   CFA
CCM   CMM   CMB   COS   LAB**

Solaray Inc.
324 S. Kidd St.
Whitewater, WI 53190
(414) 473-2525
Product codes: **AHE   AHW   CFA
CFL   FEA   APO   STA   SYA
SYL   COS   CCM   CMA   CMH
CMP   CMB**

Sun Stone Solar Energy Equipment
P.O. Box 941
Sheboygan, WI 53081
(414) 452-8194
Product codes: **AHE   CFA   FEA
AHW   CCM   COS   COC   STA
STC   SYA   APO   STL   CMB
CMM**

WYOMING

Park Energy Co.
Box SR9
Jackson, WY 83001
(307) 733-4950
Product codes: **CFA   STA   AHE
AHW**

North American Solar Incentives

The following table lists solar information agencies for all of the U.S. and Canada. As well, there is an indication of the types of incentives in effect. You should also inquire about voluntary solar easements. That is, many states now allow you to purchase rights to sunshine from a neighbor willing to sell them to you, and these rights may be transferable to anyone who may buy your property.

SOURCES FOR MORE INFORMATION	SALES TAX EXEMPT.	PROP-ERTY TAX EXEMPT.	INCOME TAX CREDIT	LOAN INCEN-TIVES
UNITED STATES				
AL Energy Mgmt. Bd.; 3734 Atlanta Hwy.; Montgomery, AL 36130. *(205) 832-5010*				
AK Div. of Energy & Power Devel.; McKay Bldg.; 7th Fl.; 338 Denali St.; Anchorage, AK 99501. *(907) 272-0527*			●	
AZ Solar Energy Rsch. Comm.; 1700 W. Washington; Phoenix, AZ 85007. *(602) 271-3682*	●	●	●	
AR Arkansas Energy Ofc.; 960 Plaza W. Bldg.; Little Rock, AR 72205. *(501) 371-1370*			●	
CA California Energy Comm.; 1111 Howe Ave.; Sacramento, CA 95825. *(916) 322-3690*			●	●
CO Ofc. of Energy Conserv.; 1410 Grant, Suite 104-B; Denver CO 80203. *(303) 839-2507*		●	●	
CT Ofc. of Policy & Mgmt., Energy Div.; 20 Grand St.; Hartford, CT 06115. *(203) 566-3395*	●	●		
DE Governor's Energy Ofc.; PO Box 1401; Townscend Bldg.; Dover, DE 19901. *(302) 678-5644*				
DC Neighborhood Improvement Admin.; Dept. of Housing & Community Devel.; 1341 G St. NW (9th floor); Washington, DC 20005.				

SOURCES FOR MORE INFORMATION	SALES TAX EXEMPT.	PROP-ERTY TAX EXEMPT.	INCOME TAX CREDIT	LOAN INCEN-TIVES
FL Florida Solar Energy Cen.; 300 State Rd.; Cape Canaveral, FL 32920. *(305) 783-0300*				
GA Georgia Ofc. of Energy Resources; Rm. 615; 270 Washington St., S.W.; Atlanta, GA.; 30334. *(404) 656-5176*	●	●		
HI Governor's Office; State Capitol; Honolulu, HI 96813.		●	●	
ID Office of Energy; State House; Boise, ID 83720. *(208) 384-3258*			●	
IL Inst. for Energy & Environ. Resources; 222 South College; Springfield, IL 62706. *(217) 782-1999*		●		
IN Indiana Dept. of Energy; 115 N. Pennsylvania; 7th Fl. Consol. Bldg.; Indianapolis, IN 46204. *(317) 633-6753*		●		
IA Energy Policy Council; 215 E. 7th St.; Des Moines, IA 50319. *(515) 281-4420*		●		
KS Kansas Energy Ofc.; 503 Kansas Ave.; Rm. 241; Topeka, KS 66603. *(913) 296-2496*		●	●	
KY Energy Ofc.; Div. of Conserv.; Capitol Plaza Tower; Frankfort, KY 40601. *(502) 564-7416*				
LA Louisiana Dept. of Natural Resources; Rsch. & Devel. Div.; P.O. Box 44156; Capitol Sta.; Baton Rouge, LA 70804. *(504) 389-2771*				
ME Maine Ofc. of Energy Resources; 55 Capitol St., Augusta, ME 04330. *(207) 289-2195*	●	●		
MD Maryland Energy Policy Ofc.; 301 W. Preston St., Rm. 1302; Baltimore, MD 21201. *(301) 383-6810*		●		
MA Solar Action Ofc.; Rm. 1413; One Ashburton Pl.; Boston, MA 02108. *(617) 727-7297*	●	●		●
MI Div. of Energy, 4th Fl.; Law Bldg.; Lansing, MI 48913. *(800) 292-4704*	●	●		
MN State Energy Agency; 740 Amer. Cen. Bldg; 9th Fl.; 150 E. Kellog; St. Paul, MN 55101. *(612) 292-8382*		●		
MS Fuel & Energy Mgmt. Comm.; 1307 Woolfolk Bldg.; Jackson, MS 39202. *(601) 354-7406*				

SOURCES FOR MORE INFORMATION	SALES TAX EXEMPT.	PROP- ERTY TAX EXEMPT.	INCOME TAX CREDIT	LOAN INCEN- TIVES
MO Missouri Energy Program; Dept. Natural Resources; P.O. Box 176; Jefferson City, MO 65101. *(314) 751-4000*				
MT Montana State Energy Ofc.; Capitol Sta.; Helena, MT 59601. *(406) 449-3940*			●	●
NE State Energy Ofc.; PO Box 95085; 301 Centennial Mall S.; Lincoln, NE 68507. *(402) 471-2867*				
NV Dept. of Energy; 1050 E. Williams; Suite 405; Capitol Complex; Carson City, NV 89710. *(702) 885-5157*		●		
NH Governor's Council on Energy; 26 Pleasant; Concord, NH 03301. *(800) 562-1115*				
NJ State Energy Ofc.; 101 Commerce St.; Newark, NJ 07102. *(201) 648-6290*	●	●		
NM Energy & Minerals Dept.; 113 Wash. Ave.; Santa Fe, NM 87501. *(505) 827-2471*		●	●	●
NY New York Energy Ofc.; Agency Bldg. 2; Empire State Plaza; Albany, NY 12223. *(518) 474-1785*		●		
NC Energy Div.; PO Box 25249; Raleigh, NC 25249. *(919) 733-2230*		●	●	
ND State Solar Ofc. Coordinator; Ofc. of Governor, State Capitol; Bismarck, ND 58505. *(701) 224-2204.*		●	●	
OH Ohio Dept. of Energy; 30 E. Broad St.; 34th Fl.; Columbus, OH 43215. *(614) 466-6797*				
OK Dept. of Energy; 4400 N. Lincoln Blvd.; Suite 251; Oklahoma City, OK 73105. *(405) 521-3941*			●	
OR Oregon Dept. of Energy; 111 Labor & Industries Bldg.; Salem, OR 97310. *(503) 378-4040*	●	●	●	●
PA Governor's Energy Council; State St. Bldg., 6th Fl.; Harrisburg, PA 17101. *(800) 882-8400*				
RI Governor's Energy Ofc.; 80 Dean St.; Providence, RI 02903. *(401) 277-3370*		●		
SC South Carolina Energy Mgmt. Ofc.; Edgar A. Brown Bldg.; Rm. 306; 1205 Pendelton St.; Columbia, SC 29201. *(800) 922-1600*				

SOURCES FOR MORE INFORMATION	SALES TAX EXEMPT.	PROP- ERTY TAX EXEMPT.	INCOME TAX CREDIT	LOAN INCEN- TIVES
SD Energy Policy Ofc.; Anderson Bldg.; Pierre, SD 57501. *(605) 224-3603*		●		
TN Tennessee Energy Authority; Suite 250; Capitol Hill Bldg.; Nashville, TN 37219. *(615) 741-2994*		●		●
TX Governor's Ofc. of Energy Resources; 7703 N. Lamar; Austin, TX 78752. *(512) 475-5491*	●			
UT Utah State Energy Ofc.; 455 E. 4th S.; Suite 303; Salt Lake City, UT 84111. *(801) 523-5424*				
VT VT State Energy Office; Montpelier, VT 05602. *(802) 828-2393*		●	●	●
VA State Energy Ofc.; 823 East Main St.; Richmond, VA 23219. *(804) 786-8451*		●		
WA State Energy Ofc.; 400 E. Union St.; 1st Fl.; Olympia, WA 98504. *(206) 753-2417*		●		
WV Fuel & Energy Ofc.; 1262½ Greenbrier St.; Charleston, WV 25311. *(304) 346-8820*				
WI Dept. of Planning & Energy; 1 West Wilson; Rm. 201; Madison, WI 53702. *(608) 266-8234*			●	
WY Energy Conservation Ofc.; Capitol Hill Ofc. Bldg.; 320 W. 25th St.; Cheyenne, WY 82002. *(307) 777-7131*				

CANADA

ALBERTA Energy Resources Conserv. Bd.; 603 6th Ave.; S.W.; Calgary, ALTA; Canada T2P OT4; Dept. of Energy & Natural Resources; Petroleum Plaza S., 9915 108 St.; Edmonton, Alta; Canada T5K 2C9.				
BC B.C. Energy Comm.; Energy Coord. Renewable Resources; #2100-1177 W. Hastings St.; Vancouver, BC; Canada V6E 2L7. *(604) 689-1831*				
MAN Manitoba Energy Council; 350 Legislative Bldg.; 450 Broadway, Winnipeg, MAN; Canada R3C OV8.				
NB New Brunswick Electric Power Comm.; 527 King St.; Fredericton, NB; Canada E3B 4X1.				

SOURCES FOR MORE INFORMATION	SALES TAX EXEMPT.	PROP- ERTY TAX EXEMPT.	INCOME TAX CREDIT	LOAN INCEN- TIVES
NEWFOUNDLAND Energy Resources Div.; Dept. of Mines & Energy; Eastern Canada Savings & Loan Bldg.; Bonaventure Ave.; St. John's, NFLD; Canada A1C 5T7.				
NS Nova Scotia Energy Council; PO Box 1087; Halifax, NS; Canada B3J 2X1. (902) 424-7680	●	●		
ONT Ontario Energy Bd.; 9th Fl.; 14 Carlton St.; Toronto, ONT; Canada M5B 1K5.	●			
Prince Edward Island Institute of Man & Resources; PO Box 2008; Charlottetown, PEI; Canada C1A 1A4.	●			
QUEBEC Directorate of New Energy Resources; Dept. of Energy; 1305, Chemin Ste-Foy; QUE; Canada PQ G1S 4N5.				
SASK Saskatchewan Research Council, 30 Campus Dr.; Saskatoon, SASK; Canada S7N OX1.				

Index